METHUEN'S MONOGRAPHS
ON BIOLOGICAL SUBJECTS

*General Editor:* KENNETH MELLANBY, C.B.E.

PLANT VIRUSES

# Plant Viruses

KENNETH M. SMITH

C.B.E., D.Sc., Ph.D., F.R.S.

*Cell Research Institute*
*University of Texas*
*in Austin*

QR351
.S63
1968

METHUEN & CO LTD
11 NEW FETTER LANE, LONDON EC4

*First published October 3, 1935*
*Second edition 1948*
*Third edition 1960*
*Fourth edition 1968*
*Printed in Great Britain by*
*Richard Clay (The Chaucer Press), Ltd.,*
*Bungay, Suffolk*

Distribution in the U.S.A.
by Barnes & Noble, Inc.

# Contents

# Plates

The plates appear between pages 86 and 87

# Preface to the Fourth Edition

The fourth edition of this small book has been rewritten and is virtually a new book. This has been made necessary by the many advances in our knowledge of plant viruses which have taken place during the comparatively few years since the publication of the third edition. In order to give even a brief account of this new knowledge, it has been necessary to omit some of that part of the previous edition which dealt with the purely practical aspects of plant virology. Another reason for this omission is the imminent publication of a multi-volume treatise dealing with every type of technique used in the study of viruses in general.

This book was rewritten during the tenure of a Visiting Professorship at the University of Texas in Austin. Grateful acknowledgement is due to Dr W. Gordon Whaley, Dean of the Graduate School, and to the Cell Research Institute for the facilities afforded to the writer.

Acknowledgement is also due to several friends who have supplied prints of illustrations from their published work; credit has been given to authors in the illustration legends.

KENNETH M. SMITH

*Cell Research Institute*
*University of Texas*
*Austin, Texas*

# CHAPTER ONE

# Introductory

Virus diseases of plants, although of course not recognized as such, were known long before the discovery of bacteria. The first record in the literature of which we have knowledge is a description published in 1576 by Charles L 'Ecluse, or Carolus Clusius, of a variegation in the colour of tulips, which is now called a 'colour-break' and is recognized to be due to an aphid-transmitted virus of the mosaic type. 'Broken' tulips are figured in *Theatrum Florae* published in 1662; these illustrations have been identified as the work of the painter Daniel Rabel. A somewhat later account published in *Traité des Tulips*, about 1670, contains the first suggestion that the variegation in the flower colour might be due to a disease. In 1715, an account of an infectious chlorosis of *Jasminum* was published in the *Art of Gardening*.

About fifty years later, the so-called 'curl disease' of potatoes came into prominence, and as to the cause of this there raged for many years a great controversy. The favourite explanation was that of 'degeneration', a kind of senile decay caused by long-continued vegetative propagation. It was pointed out, however, that in certain secluded districts, high up on mountains or in wind-blown areas near the sea, it was possible to grow the same variety of potato for many years, saving the 'seed' each year from the current year's crop, without any sign of degeneration.

It was the discovery that potato leaf-roll was an infectious virus disease which finally settled this controversy and showed that the degeneration of the potato crop was due solely to a gradual infiltration of viruses into the stocks.

About the year 1868, the variegated plant *Abutilon*, probably *A. striatum* var. *Thompsonii*, appeared in Europe and became popular as an ornamental plant. By grafting scions of variegated plants to green shoots of unvariegated plants it was shown that this variegation was infectious. Now the condition is known to be due to a virus infection transmitted by a species of whitefly.

In 1886, Mayer described a disease of the tobacco plant which he called *Mosaikkrankheit*, and this term, or its English equivalent, is now widely used to describe the mottling type of virus disease. Mayer showed that this mosaic disease of tobacco could be communicated to a healthy tobacco plant by inoculation with the sap of the infected plant. Two years later, Erwin F. Smith proved that the disease known as 'peach yellows' was also communicable and could be transmitted by budding.

It was not, however, till 1892 that the first scientific proof of the existence of a virus was given. Iwanowski (1892) working with the mosaic disease of tobacco, described by Mayer, proved that sap from such a diseased plant was capable of inducing the mosaic disease in healthy plants *after* it had passed through a bacteria-proof filter candle and was bacteriologically sterile. Curiously enough, Iwanowski himself did not seem to grasp the true significance of this and his discovery passed almost unnoticed until the work was repeated some years later by Beijerinck (1898). He made a more detailed study of the problem and showed that the agent would diffuse through agar. Because of this, Beijerinck came to the conclusion that it could not be 'corpuscular', and suggested that it was a *'contagium vivum fluidum'*. This was important as being an effort to visualize an unusual disease agent and also because it made the first step away from the fashionable bacteriology of that time, when it was thought that all infectious diseases were caused by visible micro-organisms.

The discovery of the relationship between viruses and insects was not made in a day, and a period of years elapsed between the time when insects were first suspected of transmitting plant viruses and the actual demonstration of this method of transmission. The first to prove experimentally the relationship between an insect and a plant virus seems to have been a Japanese farmer, Hashimoto, who worked in 1894 with the dwarf disease of rice and the leafhopper *Nephotettix apicalis* var. *cincticeps*. However, this information was not available to the western world for many years.

About 1907, three workers in America – Ball, Adams, and Shaw – suggested that there was some connexion between curly-top of sugar-beet and the leafhopper *Eutettix tenella*. Some years later, Smith and Boncquet (1915) confirmed this and showed that a single insect from an infected plant placed on a healthy plant for 5 minutes would produce the disease.

During the last decade much more information on the relationships of plant viruses with their vectors has been obtained. It is known now that it is not only insects which transmit plant viruses, and it is no exaggeration to state that almost any kind of organism which preys on plants is concerned in this relationship. Thus, in addition to insects of various kinds, mites, nematode worms, and fungal spores have all been incriminated as vectors, and, in several cases, not merely as mechanical instruments of transmission.

Other advances in the study of plant viruses, since the last edition of this book was published, include increased knowledge of incomplete viruses and the discovery of satellite viruses. Improvements in fixation and staining techniques for electron microscopy have led to an intensive study of viruses *in situ* in the cells of both virus-infected plants and insect vectors.

The tide of molecular biology has now reached the shores of plant virology, and more exact knowledge of the ultrastructure of both anisometric and isometric viruses has been obtained by electron microscopy and X-ray diffraction. A photographic rotation technique to enhance the detail of high-resolution electron micrographs has been devised. Further studies by X-ray diffraction have been made on the exact location of the nucleic acid on one of the very small isometric viruses, and the nucleic acid of the wound tumour virus has been shown to be double-stranded.

## Virus Characteristics

To conclude this introductory chapter, some definitions of a virus are appended. The following characteristics of viruses which separate them from all other agents are quoted from Lwoff and Tournier (1966).

(1) Virions possess only one type of nucleic acid, either deoxyribonucleic acid (DNA) or ribonucleic acid (RNA); other agents possess both types.

(2) Virions are reproduced from their sole nucleic acid, whereas other agents are reproduced from the integrated sum of their constituents.

(3) Virions are unable to grow or to undergo binary fission.

(4) Absence in the viruses of the genetic information for the synthesis of the Lipman system, the system responsible for the production of energy with high potential.

(5) Viruses make use of the ribosomes of their host cells; this is defined as absolute parasitism.

These features, being absent in other agents, are characteristic of viruses; they are present in all viruses, but absent in all nonviruses such as bacteria, and including the agents of psittacosis, protozoa, etc.

Bawden (1964), however, considers this list as too exclusive and as demanding more knowledge than there is about the constitution and behaviour of most plant viruses. He suggests instead as a definition the following: 'Viruses are sub-microscopic, infective entities that multiply only intracellularly and are potentially pathogenic.'

On the other hand, Hahon (1964) considers the older and descriptive definitions, based on size, pathogenicity, and obligate parasitism, to be inadequate. Viruses have been envisioned now as transmitters or vehicles of information-bearing genetic material or, stated in more general terms, as 'bits of infectious heredity in search of a chromosome'.

## References

BAWDEN, F. C. (1964) *Plant Viruses and Virus Diseases*. 4th ed. New York: Ronald Press Co.

BEIJERINCK, M. W. (1898) *Verhandel K. Akad. Wetensch. Amsterdam*, Sec. 2, Deel 6, 1–22.

HAHON, N. (1964) *Selected Papers on Virology*. New York: Prentice-Hall Inc.

IWANOWSKI, D. (1892) *St. Petersb. Acad. Imp. Sci. Bull.* **35**, 67–70.

L'ECLUSE, C. DE (1576) *Rariorum Aliquot Stirpium per Hispanias Observatorum Historia*. pp. 529 illus. Antwerpiae.

LWOFF, A. and TOURNIER, P. (1966) *Ann. Rev. Microbiol.* **20**, 46–74.

MAYER, A. E. (1882) *Woorloopie Meded. Landbou. Tidschr.* 359–64.

SMITH, R. E. and BONCQUET, P. A. (1915) *Phytopathology.* **5**, 103–7.

# CHAPTER TWO

# Symptomatology of Virus-infected Plants

---

When it is remembered that there are more than three hundred different viruses, not counting strains, which affect plants, it is not surprising that this multiplicity is reflected in an equally varied response by the host.

Abnormalities develop in all parts of infected plants, not only externally but internally as well, and we shall deal with these in two separate categories.

## External Symptoms

As a rule it is in the foliage of a plant that the most noticeable symptoms develop, and the effects of different viruses on the leaves take many forms. First, there is the large group of *mosaic diseases*; this name was originated by Mayer in 1882 to describe the mottling of the leaves of tobacco plants infected by the first virus to be discovered now known as tobacco mosaic virus (TMV). There are many variants of mosaic diseases; the commonest type consists of dark-green, light-green, or yellow areas on the leaves often accompanied by raised blister-like spots. As a rule the leaf itself is distorted by crinkling of the edges; this is particularly noticeable in a composite disease of the potato plant known as 'crinkle'.

Some viruses which cause a mosaic disease on one host give rise to an entirely different type of symptom on another. Examples of this are the so-called 'ringspots', sometimes called 'target spots'. The rings formed on the leaves may be single, or several concentrically situated; there is usually a central spot. The rings may be either chlorotic or necrotic, frequently the latter, and many of these ringspot viruses are transmitted by soil-living organisms (see Chapter Seven). Occasionally both rings and mosaic mottling occur together as with potato virus X on tobacco, especially in cases of manual infection of the plant.

There are some viruses which produce a mosaic mottling so bright that it resembles a variegation; examples are turnip yellow mosaic virus (Plate 1), and *Abutilon* mosaic virus.

Ring-and-line patterns or 'oakleaf' designs are common in some mosaic-type diseases.

In the virus diseases of cereals or of plants with elongated leaves, pattern formations consist of longitudinal streaks or stripes as in 'cocksfoot streak' or wheat-striate mosaic.

Since the veins of a leaf are the site of more rapid movement of virus, there are symptoms specifically associated with them in certain diseases. For example, infection of tobacco with potato virus Y produces characteristic dark-green areas along the veins which give a 'vein-banding' effect. 'Clearing' of the veins of the young leaves, especially in tobacco plants, is a common first symptom of infection with mosaic diseases; this is a transitory symptom and disappears after a few days. In tobacco veinal necrosis, however, which is caused by a virus closely related to potato virus Y, the effect is permanent and highly injurious to the plant.

One of two viruses found associated together in the composite disease known as 'tobacco rosette' causes extreme distorting and malformation of the veins. There is no mottling connected with this virus and the only visible external effect seems to be on the veins of the leaf.

Changes in leaf colour, as distinct from mottling, are symptomatic of some virus infections. A deeper green is associated with peach 'phony' disease and Fiji disease of sugar cane, and a bluish-green in 'blue dwarf' of oats.

In the Jassid-transmitted group of viruses known as 'yellows', the newly developing foliage is chlorotic especially in 'aster yellows'. This should not be confused with the aphid-borne virus causing 'sugar-beet yellows', in which mainly the outer older leaves become yellow.

In the virus disease of tomatoes known as 'spotted wilt,' a characteristic metallic bronzing of the upper leaves develops.

Distortion and malformation of the leaf itself are common symptoms; in potato leaf-roll the leaves become thick and leathery, owing to starch accumulation, and roll upwards. In some varieties of potato there is also a purplish coloration of the leaves.

Under certain conditions, when infected with cucumber mosaic virus and some strains of tobacco mosaic virus, the leaves of tomato plants take on a 'fern-leaf' or 'shoe-string' appearance owing to the suppression of the leaf lamina.

Outgrowths from the leaf blade also occur; these are known as 'enations' and are associated with pea enation mosaic, and some strains of tobacco mosaic and cucumber mosaic viruses on *Nicotiana* spp. Quite large enations are produced on the leaves of cucumber plants, var. 'Telegraph', when infected with the tomato black-ring virus.

There are many other leaf abnormalities caused by virus infections, only a few of which can be mentioned here. Leaves are tattered in the peach X disease and perforated in cherry 'tatter leaf'; they are reduced in size in the 'witches' broom' diseases of potato and black locust and in the 'little leaf' disease of eggplant. They are thickened and crumpled in sugar-beet curly-top, potato yellow dwarf, and tobacco rosette.

Abnormalities in the flowers are associated with some virus infections; of these, changes in the colour of the flowers are common. The most familiar, perhaps, is the 'tulip break' in which the flower of the self-coloured tulip is flecked or streaked with yellow. These 'broken' flowers, as they are called, can be very attractive.

A similar colour break occurs in the blood-red wallflower (*Cheiranthus*) when infected with the virus of cabbage black ringspot. The flowers of Chinese cabbage which are normally yellow are sometimes turned white by turnip yellow mosaic virus, presumably by suppression of the pigment.

In the 'yellows' type of disease virescence or greening of the flower petals is characteristic.

In addition to colour changes, other flower abnormalities occur; these may be reduction in the size or number or the precocious growth of some flower parts. In tomato big bud, the enlarged sepals fuse to form a bladder-like structure. The manner of growth also may be changed; in aster yellows, for example, and in cranberry false blossom, the flowers are erect instead of pendant.

The fruit may be affected in various ways; in cucumber plants infected with mosaic, the fruits are small, misshapen, and bumpy.

B

Tomato fruits frequently show mottling when infected with tomato mosaic, or concentric rings when infected with spotted wilt or bushy stunt viruses. In the red suture disease of peach trees, the peaches are often misshapen, and they have an insipid flavour in the 'little peach' disease.

The stems also show a variety of symptoms, the internode length may be reduced or the number of stems greatly increased as in the 'witches' broom' type of disease. In some tree infections, the bark may be cracked or cankered or scaled away as in the exocortis disease of citrus. In the 'rubbery wood' disease of apple, rigidity of the stems is lost as a result of the lack of lignification.

Root symptoms have been less studied than symptoms in other parts of virus-affected plants, but certain abnormalities are known. In corn stunt disease, the roots are much shorter than normal and are bunchy in Fiji disease of the sugar cane.

Tumours form on the roots of *Rumex* or sweet clover plants infected with the wound tumour virus. Death of the roots occurs in the citrus tristeza disease, and in phloem necrosis of elm trees. In the latter, there is a brownish discoloration with a faint odour of wintergreen. For a more complete description of the external symptoms, the reader is referred to Holmes (1964).

**Internal Symptoms**

Various changes can be observed in the histology of virus-infected leaves, especially in diseases causing leaf distortion as in potato leaf-roll and lily rosette where marked phloem necrosis occurs. In sugar-beet curly-top, there is degeneration of the phloem accompanied by supernumerary sieve tubes. Perhaps the most interesting internal symptoms are the so-called 'intracellular inclusions'. There is quite a large literature on this subject dating from Iwanovski's description in 1903 of the crystalline bodies in the cells of tobacco plants infected with tobacco mosaic virus. These intracellular inclusions occur only in plants affected with a virus and so can be of diagnostic value. Their absence, however, does not necessarily mean that no virus is present.

Matz (1919), Kunkel (1921), and Smith (1924) were among the first workers to observe these inclusions and for some time a controversy centred about their nature. One school of thought considered them to be organisms, possibly related to the protozoa, while the other group thought they were some effect of the disordered metabolism of the cell. In retrospect it is interesting to consider that those who considered the inclusions to be the cause of the disease were nearer to the truth, though not in the sense of the organism they visualized. There seems now to be little doubt that some at least of these inclusions are aggregates of virus particles large enough to be seen in the optical microscope.

There are two main types of inclusions, crystalline and amorphous; the latter are known as X-bodies. In addition there occur in the cytoplasm of infected cells bizarre structures in the shape of 'pinwheels' and 'cat-o-nine-tails' (Plate 2). These bodies are symptomatic of infection by flexuous rod-shaped viruses of the potato virus Y group (Edwardson, 1966 a and b) but their exact nature is not known; it seems unlikely that they consist of virus. On the other hand they seem to have a very close connexion with the endoplasmic reticulum (Arnott and Smith, 1967).

It was first pointed out by Purdy-Beale (1937) that the crystalline inclusions in tobacco mosaic closely resembled the paracrystals of tobacco mosaic virus first isolated by Stanley (1935).

Inclusion bodies are most common in the epidermal cells of leaves and stems, but they also occur in the roots and flowers and in most tissues except the phloem sieve elements (Bawden, 1964).

McWhorter (1965) has tabulated the various types of intracellular inclusions as follows.

*Group* A. Amorphous inclusions only, crystalline inclusions absent.

*Group* B. Amorphous and crystalline inclusions; crystals in the cytoplasm, seldom or never present in the nucleus.

*Group* C. Amorphous and crystalline inclusions; crystals present in both nuclei and cytoplasm.

*Group* D. Other entities unusual or only described in part.

*Examples. Group* A. Amorphous spherules in wound tumour disease of *Rumex acetosa. Group* B. Tobacco mosaic virus in tobacco, red clover vein mosaic virus in *Vicia faba. Group* C. Tobacco etch virus in Solanaceae; to which, perhaps, may be added in *Group* D, the 'pinwheels' shown in Plate 2 which occur in virus-infected cells of the wild sunflower (Arnott and Smith, 1967).

A somewhat similar grouping of the intracellular inclusions is suggested by Matsui and Yamaguchi (1966). According to the light microscope, the inclusions fall into four groups, X-bodies which are cytoplasmic amorphous or amoeboid inclusions, cytoplasmic crystalline inclusions, intranuclear inclusions, and other types of inclusion.

Sheffield (1946) showed that a preparation of X-bodies was about as infective as solutions containing the same weight of purified virus as the computed weight of the X-bodies. She also showed by means of electron microscopy that they contained many virus rods.

*X-bodies*

Those associated with tobacco mosaic are divided by Matsui (1959) into two categories based upon their fine structure. One usually appears elliptical in outline and is almost entirely composed of dense granules varying in size; there is no envelope. The other usually appears spherical in outline and consists of a narrow peripheral zone and large internal vacuole.

So far as these two types of X-bodies are concerned, some have masses of virus particles adsorbed on the surface while others do not. They are not thought to occlude virus particles.

According to Matsui (1959) some of the crystalline inclusions are formed from virus particles adhering to the surface of the X-body, while others are formed within the cytoplasm.

Some studies have been made on X-bodies associated with other viruses. Those associated with tobacco etch virus on *Datura stramonium* have been investigated by Matsui and Yamaguchi (1964a). The X-body in this case consists of a dense peripheral zone and an internal matrix. The peripheral zone consists of lipid drops while the internal matrix seems to be cytoplasm containing virus particles and some cytoplasmic organelles.

Cells of *Pisum sativum* infected with red clover vein-mosaic virus showed X-bodies which contained coiled filamentous particles (Rubio-Huertos, 1964).

X-bodies were picked out by means of a glass needle from cells in epidermal strips of plants infected with broad-bean mottle virus and cabbage black ringspot virus. These were examined in the electron microscope and found to consist mainly of virus particles (Rubio-Huertos and van Slogteren, 1956; Rubio-Huertos, 1956).

Similarly, sections of X-bodies, viewed in the electron microscope, are mainly composed of virus (Black, Morgan, and Wyckoff, 1950; Nixon and Sampson, 1954).

Examination of various types of X-bodies on the electron microscope suggests that while some contain virus particles others do not.

### Cytoplasmic Crystalline Inclusions

Investigation of the crystalline inclusions in tobacco mosaic was difficult because of their tendency to disintegrate when touched with a glass needle or fixed for sectioning. However, this difficulty was overcome by Steere and Williams (1953), who extracted the inclusions intact by means of a freeze-drying technique. They were then placed in a drop of water on a grid and examined in the electron microscope; they appeared to consist almost entirely of virus particles.

Intracellular inclusions seem to be associated only with rod-shaped virus particles. No inclusion bodies have been described in connexion with 'spherical' viruses, although microcrystals of tomato bushy stunt virus have been observed in the cells of infected *Datura stramonium* (Smith, 1956).

### Intranuclear Inclusions

These are not common but do occur, the best known being associated with tobacco etch and bean yellow mosaic viruses. Kassanis (1939) and Bawden and Kassanis (1941) have described crystalline inclusions in the nuclei of tobacco cells infected with severe etch virus. These inclusions are mainly in the form of thin plates, birefringent when seen from the edge; their occurrence is sufficiently regular as to be of diagnostic value.

The same inclusions have been studied by Matsui and Yamaguchi (1964 a and b), who state that they differ from the nucleolus, nuclear matrix, and chromatin in both morphology and density. They were unable to detect any virus or virus-like patterns within the inclusions. On the other hand, Rubio-Hertos and Hidalgo (1964), who have also studied severe etch infections, find that the intranuclear inclusions can be resolved into a stack of dense lines, arranged parallel to the long axis of the inclusion, which are assumed to be bundles of virus particles.

Intranuclear crystalline inclusions have been observed within leaves of *Vicia faba* or *Phaseolus vulgaris* infected with bean yellow mosaic virus.

The inclusions occurred frequently in groups in the nucleoplasm, whereas they usually occurred singly within the nucleolus, and were so large as to distort it. The inclusions revealed a regular periodicity of striation within them. The cytoplasm also contained similar crystalline inclusions (Weintraub and Ragetli, 1965). There seems to be no evidence that the intranuclear inclusions consist of, or contain, virus, other than what has been observed in the electron microscope.

*Other Types of Inclusion*
Various kinds of rather peculiar inclusions, associated with virus infection, can be placed in this category. There are the spindle bodies found in virus-affected cacti, and the bizarre 'pin-wheels' and 'cat-o-nine-tails' previously mentioned. Crystalline inclusions within some chloroplasts of *Beta vulgaris* infected with beet yellows virus or western yellows virus have been reported. If this type of inclusion should be found to consist of virus, this would be some evidence that virus might be produced within the host cell chloroplasts (Engelbrecht and Esau, 1963).

## References

ARNOTT, H. A. and SMITH, K. M. (1967) *J. Ultrastruct. Res.* **19**, 173–95.
BAWDEN, F. C. (1964) *Plant Viruses and Virus Disease.* 4th ed. New York: Ronald Press Co.
BAWDEN, F. C. and KASSANIS, B. (1941) *Ann. appl. Biol.* **28**, 107.
BEALE, H. PURDY. (1937) *Contr. Boyce Thompson Inst. Pl. Res.* **8**, 415–31.
BLACK, L. M., MORGAN, C., and WYCKOFF, R. W. G. (1950) *Proc. Soc. Exptl. Biol. Med.* **73**, 119.
EDWARDSON, J. R. (1966a) *Science.* **153**, 883–4.
EDWARDSON, J. R. (1966b) *Amer. J. Bot.* **53**, 359.
ENGELBRECHT, A. H. P. and ESAU, K. (1963) *Virology.* **21**, 43.
HOLMES, F. O. (1964) 'Symptomatology of viral diseases in plants'. *Plant Virology.* pp. 17–38. Eds. M. K. Corbett and H. D. Sisler. Gainesville: Univ. of Florida Press.
IWANOWSKI, D. (1903) *Z. Pflanzenkr.* **13**, 1–14.
KASSANIS, B. (1939) *Ann. appl. Biol.* **26**, 705–9.
KUNKEL, L. O. (1921) *Hawaiian Sug. Plant. Assoc. Exp. Sta. Bot. Ser. Bul.* **3**, 1–14.
MATSUI, C. (1959) *Virology.* **9**, 306–13.
MATSUI, C. and YAMAGUCHI, A. (1964a) *Virology.* **22**, 40.
MATSUI, C. and YAMAGUCHI, A. (1964b) *Virology.* **23**, 346.

MATSUI, C. and YAMAGUCHI, A. (1966) *Adv. Vir. Res.* **12**, 127–74.

MATZ, J. (1919) *J. Dept. Agric. Puerto Rico.* **3**, 65–82.

MAYER, G. E. (1882) *Woorloopie Meded. Landbou. Tidschr.* 359–64.

McWHORTER, F. P. (1965) *Ann. Rev. Phytopathol.* **3**, 287–312.

NIXON, H. L. and SAMPSON, J. (1954) *Proc. Internat. Conf. Electron Microscopy.* London, *Roy. Microscop. Soc.* p. 251.

RUBIO HUERTOS, M. (1956) *Phytopathology.* **46**, 553–6.

RUBIO HUERTOS, M. (1964) *Microbiol. Espan.* **17**, 1.

RUBIO HUERTOS, M. and HIDALGO, F. G. (1964) *Virology.* **24**, 84.

RUBIO HUERTOS, M. and VAN SLOGTEREN, D. H. M. (1956) *Phytopathology.* **46**, 401–2.

SHEFFIELD, F. M. L. (1946) *J. Roy. Microscop. Soc.* **66**, 69.

SMITH, K. M. (1924) *Ann. Bot.* **38**, 385.

SMITH, K. M. (1956) *Virology.* **2**, 706.

STANLEY, W. M. (1935) *Science. N. S.* **81**, 644–5.

STEERE, R. S. and WILLIAMS, R. C. (1953) *Amer. J. Bot.* **40**, 81–4.

WEINTRAUB, M. and RAGETLI, H. W. (1965) *Phytopathology.* **55**, 1082 (Abstr.).

# CHAPTER THREE

# Physiology of Plant Virus Diseases

## Metabolism of Virus-infected Plants

### Respiration

In the past a great deal of work has been done on the respiration of virus-diseased plants, much of it with tobacco mosaic virus. The results, however, have been confusing and often contradictory, chiefly because there are so many variable factors not taken into account by the earlier workers. Owen (1955b) points out that the variability in respiration rate between comparable leaves of similarly treated plants is so great, even when plants are selected for uniformity of size and appearance, that many replications are necessary to establish unequivocally the nature and magnitude of the effect of infection. Owen's experiments on the respiration rates of mosaic-infected tobacco leaves show that these rates can be higher or lower than, or identical with, those of healthy leaves depending upon: (a) the time after inoculation; (b) the physiological state of the plants; (c) the environmental conditions during growth; (d) the leaves chosen; or (e) the mode of expression of the results. In future work on respiration rates of virus-diseased plants, it will be necessary to take these facts into consideration and also to apply adequate statistical tests of significance to any differences obtained.

The effect of infection with tobacco mosaic virus on the respiration rates of detached tobacco leaves, in the period immediately after inoculation, differed in plants grown at different times of the year. During winter, infection increased respiration rates and in summer decreased them. In winter-grown plants, increasing the light intensity during the period before inoculation decreased respiration rates after infection.

Respiration rates began to change in less than one hour after inoculation and are unlikely to be associated with the formation of new virus.

These variations and contradictions are equally conspicuous when plants systemically infected with tobacco mosaic virus are studied. Thus, the rate of $CO_2$ production per gramme of dry matter of the younger leaves of tobacco plants, systemically infected with tobacco mosaic virus, was about 10 per cent less than that of comparable healthy leaves. Older infected leaves, with well-developed mosaic symptoms, had the same respiration rate as comparable healthy leaves. The effects of the virus on the water content were so great that the rate of $CO_2$ production per gramme fresh weight was sometimes significantly increased by infection (Owen, 1955 a and b, 1956).

On the other hand, another virus may affect the respiration of the same plant in quite a different way. For example, unlike tobacco mosaic virus, which increases the respiration of tobacco leaves within an hour of being inoculated, the virus of tobacco severe etch did not change the respiration rates until the leaves showed external symptoms. The respiration rates of inoculated or systemically infected leaves with symptoms rose to 40 per cent above that of healthy leaves, three times the increase produced by tobacco mosaic virus. Moreover, the increased respiration rate occurred at all times of the year and was maintained throughout the life of the leaves (Owen, 1957).

In the case of potato leaf-roll, the respiration rates are higher in the diseased than in the healthy plant. According to Whitehead (1934), except for a short period covering the end of dormancy of the tuber to the first unfolding of the leaves, the leaf-roll-infected potato plant respires at a much higher rate than does the healthy one. He concluded that the virus affects the respiration rate not directly, but only by interfering with the translocation of the respirable substrate.

*Effects on Photosynthesis*

There seems to be some difference of opinion as to whether virus infection destroys the chlorophyll or inhibits its formation. In any case there is little doubt that decreased photosynthetic activity arises from virus infection. Sheffield (1933) considered that the virus of tomato aucuba mosaic did not affect the chloroplasts of leaves fully developed at the time of infection, but did prevent the formation of plastids in young growing leaves. On the other hand, some viruses, such as those of cucumber mosaic and tomato stripe, do produce chlorosis when rubbed over mature leaves (Smith, 1935). It is possible that both may be true according to the virus concerned. Cook (1947) considers that the virus competes with the plastids for some of the products necessary for their existence, such as phosphorus and nitrogen, but does not destroy them. It is probable, however, that the pathological effect is more complicated than Cook suggests. In the case of potato aucuba mosaic Clinch (1932) considers that the yellow spots are mainly due to the loss of green pigment, to excessive quantities of starch in the plastids, and to alterations in the structure of the chloroplasts which frequently disintegrate.

In his review of the physiology of virus-infected plants, Diener (1963) suggests the following conclusions.

(1) It appears that deficiencies of nonprotein nitrogen compounds occur during intense synthesis of viruses that reach high titres, particularly under conditions of nitrogen deficiency. Under conditions of nitrogen stress, normal proteins are hydrolysed and the resulting nitrogen is apparently used for virus synthesis. Thus, virus synthesis occurs indirectly at the expense of normal protein. With viruses reaching only low titres, such deficiencies do not occur during virus synthesis.

(2) In yellows-type virus diseases, underground parts of diseased plants are richer in nitrogenous constituents than comparable parts of healthy plants, whereas leaves from diseased plants are deficient in total nitrogen and protein nitrogen content but may contain increased amounts of soluble nitrogen as compared with healthy leaves.

(3) With many virus diseases, an accumulation of nonprotein nitrogen compounds, particularly of amides, occurs in diseased leaves.

In conclusion, Diener (1963) considers that the physiological derangements most commonly associated with plant virus infection are as follows: (a) decreased photosynthetic activity; (b) increased rate of respiration; (c) accumulation of soluble nitrogen compounds, particularly amides; (d) increased activity of polyphenoloxidase and accumulation of oxidized polyphenol derivatives; (e) decreased activity of growth-regulating substances.

## Translocation of the Virus in the Plant

In considering first the transport of virus from cell to cell, it seems clear that two kinds of movement must be visualized. There is first the slow cell-to-cell movement via the connecting protoplasmic bridges or plasmodesms; such a movement presumably takes place following the infection, for example, of a trichome with tobacco mosaic virus. As regards the cell-to-cell movement of virus via the plasmodesms, a paper by Kassanis, Tinsley, and Quak (1958) is relevant. While not denying the role of the plasmodesms in virus movement, they suggest that viruses may move from cell to cell by other means. This conclusion is based on the results of tissue culture work with tobacco mosaic virus; they found that the virus moved from cell to cell at the rate of 1 mm per week in tobacco callus in the absence of plasmodesms. It is possible that the endoplasmic reticulum (ER) may connect one cell to another through the plasmodesmata (Buvat, 1957; Livingston, 1964).

On the other hand Esau, et al. (1967) have published electron micrographs showing large numbers of particles of beet yellows virus in the act of passing through the plasmodesms (Plate 3).

The rate of cell-to-cell movement is probably governed by a number of factors, including the rate of the circulatory movement of protoplasm within a cell, the rate of production of infectious units within a cell, and the number of available cell exits in the form of plasmodesms (Rappaport and Wildman. 1957).

Schneider (1965) considers that there is no movement from cells of virus particles which do not infect after mechanical inoculation. Rappaport and Wildman (loc. cit.) studied the spread of local lesions produced by three different strains of tobacco mosaic virus as a function of time. Each strain had its own characteristic spreading rate, and the three rates were uniform in time. A direct proportionality was observed between lesion area and extractable infectious material associated with two of the three strains. The strict proportionality between the amount of infectious material and the area into which the virus had spread was interpreted as suggesting a continuous and direct cell-to-cell invasion.

The second kind of movement is the more rapid one via the phloem, probably in the sieve tubes. In some cases the virus may be confined to the xylem. The virus causing Pierce's disease of grapes, now known to be the same as that of alfalfa dwarf disease, is transmitted only by leafhoppers which feed in the xylem. If the insects are prevented mechanically from reaching the xylem, infection does not occur (Houston, Esau, and Hewitt, 1947).

In the first type of slow cell-to-cell movement, the virus is presumably carried round the cell by diffusion and protoplasmic streaming, passing via the plasmodesms or by holes in the cell wall from cell to cell. It seems clear that viruses cannot pass through the cell wall by diffusion. In the more rapid movement in the phloem, these forces presumably play no part, but viruses have been shown to move rapidly in directions of food utilization and storage and slowly in opposite directions. Bennett (1960) experimented with three viruses using triple-crown sugar-beets and found a correlation between virus movement and food translocation. The experiments also gave a comparison of the rates of movement of the three viruses. The triple-crown beets favoured the rapid movement of all three viruses, but there was considerable delay when each virus had to travel from the same inoculated shoot into a non-defoliated shoot. The time of appearance of the symptoms in the non-defoliated shoot, and presumably the rate of virus movement, varied considerably. The mosaic virus moved the most rapidly producing symptoms in the shortest time averaging about 34 days, the yellows virus required an average of 57 days, whereas the curly-top virus had not produced symptoms in as long as 140 days.

Viruses confined to the parenchyma would obviously be greatly handicapped in their movement through the plant, and it is probably only in local lesions formed by some viruses on certain plants that this relationship holds good. Of viruses confined to the phloem, those of curly-top of sugar-beet and raspberry leaf-curl (American) have been studied by Bennett (1927). He has shown that these viruses may be confined to certain parts of a plant by destroying the phloem connexions between the inoculated portion and other parts of the plant at the time of inoculation. Caldwell (1930) carried out a similar experiment with tomato plants and the virus of tomato mosaic. A 'bridge' was made in the stem by means of steam, so that only the xylem vessels were left; it was found that when inoculation was made the virus remained in the half of the plant inoculated and was unable to pass the xylem 'bridge'. Caldwell (1934) also claimed that, when virus was injected into the xylem vessels, it could not escape therefrom unless the vessels were mechanically injured, whereupon the leaves of the isolated portion of the plant developed symptoms.

There is some controversy as to the actual form in which the virus particle is translocated. Is it as a whole particle or as naked ribonucleic acid? The suggestion has been made that the plasmodesms were too small to allow passage of some of the rod-shaped viruses, such as that of tobacco mosaic. In view, however, of the work of Esau *et al.* (1967), who, as already mentioned, have published electron micrographs showing the passage of whole virus, the rod-shaped beet yellows virus, through the plasmodesms, it must be assumed that whole virus can be translocated at all events in some cases. In this connexion see also the work of Shalla (1959) and Livingston (1964).

There is, however, some evidence that intact virus particles are not present during the earliest stages of multiplication of the virus. These results are based on radiation and inactivation studies (Zech and Vogt-Köhne, 1956; Rappaport and Wildman, 1957).

Siegel *et al.* (1962) have investigated two incomplete forms of tobacco mosaic virus. One fails to synthesize virus protein, and the other synthesizes the protein but it fails to form a complete particle. The movement of these incomplete particles in the cell may throw some light on the question as to whether translocation of virus in the form of nucleic acid alone can take place. It appears from this work that the nucleic acid alone can only move leaf by leaf with no transport in the phloem.

## Interference between Viruses

It is a commonplace now in plant virus research that plants, and this includes woody plants like stone-fruit trees, are frequently infected with a complex of viruses rather than with one virus alone. From this has arisen a realization of the somewhat involved interactions which may take place when two or more viruses are acting together in the same host. This subject has been reviewed by Bennett (1953) and more recently by Kassanis (1963), to whom the reader is referred for a more detailed account.

Perhaps the first realization that viruses infecting the same host plant reacted upon each other was the discovery of the so-called 'acquired immunity' against further virus infection or 'cross-protection' as it is more usually called.

This phenomenon was thought at one time to be restricted to strains of the same virus or at least to viruses having many properties in common.

Kassanis (1963), however, concludes that, based on present knowledge, interference is more complete, but not necessarily of a different type, between strains than between unrelated viruses, and that more evidence is needed to decide whether the interference is also most frequent between strains.

The ability of one virus strain to inhibit the entrance of another strain of the same virus into the same plant was first demonstrated by McKinney (1929). He showed that plants infected with a strain of tobacco mosaic virus which gave rise to a light-green mosaic underwent no change in symptoms after repeated inoculations with a strain of virus causing a yellow mosaic. In 1931, Thung carried out a similar experiment with a strain of tobacco mosaic virus causing a white mosaic against the ordinary green mottling type. The same cross-protection phenomenon was also demonstrated by Salaman (1933) using different strains of potato virus X on *Datura stramonium*. It appeared at first from those experiments that a useful means of recognition of relationship between viruses was thus available. However, more work has not supported this hope, and the best that can be said for the method is that a relationship between two viruses can be presumed when there is cross-protection, but the absence of this phenomenon does not imply that the viruses are unrelated. Indeed, the range of reactions between related viruses in the same plant is very wide. Bennett (1953) has classified this range into: (*a*) high degree of protection; (*b*) intermediate degree of protection; (*c*) low degree of protection. In the first category are mostly mosaic and ringspot-type viruses such as cucumber mosaic virus in cowpea and zinnia (Price, 1939; Fulton, 1950), and some strains of tobacco ringspot virus (Price, 1932; Tall, Price, and Westmann, 1949). The second category is well represented by potato virus X, which could also be included in the first category because of its variable behaviour in cross-protection. Thus Smith (1933) demonstrated the failure of a mottle strain to protect against a necrotic ringspot strain, and Bawden and Sheffield (1944) found that potato plants infected with virus X were not completely protected against potato virus B. Similarly, Hutton (1948) tested a number of strains of potato virus X, some of which gave complete cross-protection and some none at all, this depending in one case on the species of host plant. Tobacco mosaic virus strains also differ in the degree of protection afforded, and necrotic-type strains sometimes produce local lesions on leaves systemically infected with a mottling strain (Fulton, 1951).

The virus that seems to have the lowest degree of interference is that of sugar-beet curly-top, and there is little evidence of any tendency to acquire resistance by one strain of this virus against another (Giddings, 1950).

There is evidence in some cases that the degree of cross-protection between like viruses is correlated with their serological reactions. Matthews (1949) working with a number of strains of potato virus X found complete protection in the plant with those strains which gave the same serological reaction, but protection was not complete with those strains which differed serologically. On the other hand, this is not always the case; it has been shown that the viruses known as cucumber viruses 3 and 4 (cucumber green mottle mosaic and cucumber aucuba mosaic viruses) have similar serological, morphological, and physical properties to tobacco mosaic virus (Bawden and Pirie, 1937; Knight and Stanley, 1941), but the presence of these viruses in the cotyledons of cucumber plants gives no protection against infection with tobacco mosaic virus (Fulton, 1951). Similarly, tobacco veinal necrosis virus is serologically related to potato viruses Y and C. It does not protect tobacco, *Nicotiana glutinosa*, or potato plants from infection by them; and tobacco and *N. glutinosa* plants infected with either virus Y or C are still susceptible to it (Bawden and Kassanis, 1951).

Some interactions also occur between unrelated viruses acting together in the same plant, and these may take various forms. Suppression of, or antagonism towards, one of the two viruses has been described in one or two cases, while in others there may be increased severity of the disease or increased virus concentration.

Bawden and Kassanis (1945) have shown that the presence of the severe etch virus in tobacco plants prevents the multiplication of the two unrelated viruses, that of henbane mosaic and potato virus Y. Moreover, the severe etch virus is able to replace the two latter viruses in the plant. Bawden and Kassanis suggest that this may be due to an effect by the etch virus on cell metabolism resulting in the suppression of production of some material or enzyme system necessary for the increase of the potato Y and henbane mosaic viruses.

Another example of this kind of antagonism between unrelated viruses has been described by Ross (1950). He found that in the potato seedling USDA 41956, which is resistant to potato virus X, lesion formation by potato virus Y was partially inhibited if the inoculum contained potato virus X. Furthermore, the number of lesions produced by virus Y was progressively reduced as the concentration of virus X in the inoculum was increased.

Garces-Orejuela and Pound (1957) state that, in plants doubly infected with cucumber and tobacco mosaic viruses, the concentration of the latter was always higher in doubly than in singly infected plants, and more so after 1 or 2 weeks than after 3 or 4 weeks. Cucumber mosaic virus was more concentrated 4 days after inoculation in singly than in doubly infected plants, but after 2 weeks this was reversed, symptoms being more severe. In each of the combinations tested, neither virus was able completely to inhibit increase of the other, and the enhanced symptoms were an additional effect.

A good example of increased severity of a disease (synergism) by a mixed virus infection is that known as 'double-virus streak' or 'glasshouse streak' of tomatoes. The two viruses concerned are that of tomato (= tobacco) mosaic and potato virus X. When occurring separately in tomato plants, the diseases caused by these two viruses are not severe, being mainly of the mottling type; when the two are acting together, however, much necrosis of the leaves and stem develops and frequently causes the death of the plant. Curiously enough, the severity of the disease does not seem to vary, even if the component viruses are very mild strains.

Similar synergistic examples are found in the potato crinkle diseases produced by the potato viruses X and Y (Smith, 1931) and A and X (Murphy and McKay, 1932).

It has been shown by Ross (1950) and his co-workers that potato or tobacco plants doubly infected with potato virus X (PVX) and with potato virus Y (PVY) contained considerably more PVX than did comparable singly infected plants. With leaves invaded while they were growing rapidly, i.e. during the acute stage of infection, ratios of 10:1 were obtained in several experiments in which the viruses were introduced together. This ratio may drop to 4:1 in leaves formed subsequent to systemic infection. There seems to be no comparable increase in concentration of the accompanying PVY.

Where there is a multiplicity of reactions, there are likely to be many different mechanisms involved and there must be competition between two viruses operating in the same cell. Ross (1959) suggests that, in the case of marked stimulation in the multiplication of a virus in a mixed infection, this may be because the second virus either supplies specific substrates or prevents the action of by-products that are formed during the synthesis of the first virus and normally act to limit its multiplication.

Interference effects can also be studied by means of local lesions (see Chapter Ten). According to McKinney (1940, 1941), the number of local lesions produced on the leaves of tobacco and *Nicotiana sylvestris* were reduced or delayed if the plants were already infected with cucumber mosaic virus. There are several instances of the reduction in the number of local lesions by interference of another virus. Sadasivan (1940) found that fewer necrotic local lesions were produced by necrosis-forming strains of tobacco mosaic virus (TMV) or potato virus X (PVX) when they were inoculated in company with a mottle-forming strain of the same virus than when they were inoculated alone. As the concentration of the mottle-forming strain in the mixed inoculum increased, so the number of lesions decreased until none were produced.

Siegel (1959) found a similar phenomenon using the $U_1$ (mottle-forming) and $U_2$ (local lesion-forming) strains of TMV, and Helms (1965) describes interference between the same two strains on leaves of the bean plant, *Phaseolus vulgaris* L. var. Pinto. Strain $U_1$, when mixed with increasing concentrations of strain $U_2$, gave fewer macroscopic lesions than did $U_1$ acting alone.

Wu and Rappaport (1961) also used $U_1$ and $U_2$ strains of TMV on Pinto beans. This variety of bean reacts with necrotic local lesions to inoculation with $U_1$, but seems to be immune to infection with $U_2$. Nevertheless, the presence of $U_2$ in the inoculum strongly inhibits the number of lesions produced by $U_1$, the degree of inhibition depending on the concentration of $U_2$.

It is possible that some interferon-like substance, produced by the cells in response to the $U_2$ virus, may play some part in reducing the number of local lesions (see 'Resistance to Infection' later in this chapter).

Thomson (1960) found a reduction in the number of local lesions

c

when he used unrelated viruses in the same host plant, only one of which gave rise to local lesions. The following results show this reduction: type strain of TMV and aucuba strain mixed inoculum 9 lesions, control 108; type strain of TMV and cabbage black ring spot virus, 3 and 38; type strain of potato virus Y and cabbage black ringspot, 2 and 38; tobacco veinal necrosis virus and type strain of potato virus Y, 19 and 64.

Thus, certain mixtures of viruses, one being a local-lesion-forming virus and the other not, when inoculated simultaneously produce fewer lesions than when inoculated singly.

The converse is also true, i.e. that certain pairs of viruses when inoculated together *increase* the number of lesions. There are numerous possible reasons for this, such as the concentration of the virus (Close, 1962), species and age of plant, and susceptibility of the plant.

Kassanis (1963) suggests that the simplest explanation for the increase in the number of lesions, when two viruses are simultaneously inoculated, might be that infection by the assisting virus activates an enzyme system needed for the local-lesion-forming virus to initiate infection, or changes the general metabolism of the cell so that the local-lesion-forming virus can multiply.

## Latent Infections

A good deal of confusion has arisen concerning the exact terms to be used to describe that phenomenon whereby an organism is infected with a virus but yet shows no apparent signs of infection. In order to clarify the situation, a symposium was held in Wisconsin on 'Latency and Masking in Viral and Rickettsial Infections' (1958), and a symposium on similar lines was held in Stockholm on the occasion of the 7th International Congress of Microbiology (1958).

The conclusions arrived at by the Wisconsin meeting are as follows.

*Inapparent infection* covers, at the host–parasite level, the whole field of infections which give no overt sign of their presence. The term 'subclinical' can be used as an alternative, particularly in human medicine.

*Latent infections* are inapparent infections which are chronic and in which a certain virus–host equilibrium is established. The adjective 'latent' is best reserved to qualify 'infection', the term 'latent virus' being avoided.

*Occult virus* is used to describe the cases where virus particles cannot be detected and in which the actual state of the virus cannot as yet be ascertained. It is preferred to 'masked', since this word has been used in a number of contradictory meanings.

Whenever it has been shown that viruses of animals or higher plants go through cycles as described for bacteriophage, and also for algal virus, the terms *provirus*, *vegetative virus*, and *infective virus* are appropriate for the corresponding stages. Infective virus is the fully formed virus particle.

A *moderate* virus is one growing in a cell while still permitting its continued survival and multiplication; a *cytocidal* one kills the cell; *submoderate* covers intermediate cases. (Some viruses may be moderate in one cell-system, cytocidal in another, as, for example, potato virus X in different potato varieties.) However, as pointed out by Lwoff (1958), in order that an infection, whether apparent or not, should be recognized as viral, infectious particles have to be detected and identified as a virus. In the present state of our knowledge, however, this would eliminate about half of the plant viruses so far recorded. In his contribution to the symposium on latency at the 7th International Congress of Microbiology, Bennett (1959) prefers the term 'masking' and defines this as a condition in which a virus is actively present in a plant without causing obvious effects, regardless of the cause of this lack of obvious effects.

On the other hand, Bawden (1958) refers to the freedom of an infected plant from visible lesions as 'commensalism'. He considers this term more appropriate, because it conveys the idea of existing together in harmony, and does not suggest, as do latency and masking, that the lack of virulence depends on some change in the state of the virus.

Smith (1952) suggests two types of latent virus infection in plants. In the first there is an initial reaction which soon disappears and the plant appears normal. Examples of this kind of infection are given by the tomato black-ring virus (Smith, 1946) and viruses of the tobacco ring-spot type. In the second category belong those viruses which never cause a disease in their original plant host and cannot apparently be made to do so. Examples of this group are the latent infection in dodder, *Cuscuta* spp. (Bennett, 1944), carnation latent infection, and the latent infection in *Fragaria vesca*.

It could be said that potato paracrinkle virus was a perfect example of this latter group were it not for one fact, i.e. that until recently no one had ever seen a potato plant of the King Edward variety without the virus with which to make comparison. Now, however, that plants of this variety have been obtained free of virus, it can be said that there are certain symptom differences between the two (Kassanis, 1957).

Although there are no apparent macroscopic differences between plants with latent virus infections and those which are virus-free, study has shown that leaf tissue may be strikingly affected chemically. In affected but outwardly symptomless leaves, patterns of starch distribution may be as revealing as the more frequently recognized patterns of chlorophyll damage (Holmes, 1964).

## Causes of Latent Infections

It is probable that the underlying causes of latency differ in the two types mentioned above. Where there is an initial reaction which is followed by the disappearance of all symptoms, the probable cause is low or reduced virus concentration as suggested by Bennett (1959), who considers that a drop in concentration may be associated with accumulation and rate of production of materials for virus synthesis. This type of latent infection can sometimes be stimulated once more to activity, for example by the addition of another virus. This is somewhat analogous to the situation in insects, where latent virus infections can on occasion be increased in virulence by inoculation with a second virus (Smith, 1967).

In tomato plants which have completely recovered, so far as outward signs are concerned, from infection with the dodder latent virus, the concentration of the virus is very low. Upon the inoculation of tobacco mosaic or tobacco streak viruses to the recovered plants, however, symptoms due to the dodder virus reappear and the concentration of this virus rises again to comparatively high levels (Bennett, 1949).

An interesting relationship exists between different types of orange and the tristeza virus. Both sweet and sour orange are highly resistant to injury when on their own roots, so that each species appears to have a high degree of tolerance of the concentration of virus it produces in its own tissues. However, experiments with aphid transfers suggest that virus concentration is much higher in the sweet than in the sour orange. When a graft is made of a sour orange top on a sweet orange rootstock, the tree remains symptom-free, but if the reverse procedure is carried out the tree is killed. When the virus concentration in the top is low and the root is tolerant, as in sour orange on sweet, no damage is caused. However, if the virus concentration in the top is high and root tolerance is low, as in the sweet orange on sour, death ensues (Bennett, 1959).

In the other type of latent infection where there has been no initial disease, addition of a second virus seems to have no stimulatory effect. The underlying causes for this type of latent infection are not known; evidently a satisfactory virus-host equilibrium has been established.

*Some Examples of Latent Virus Infections*

One of the earliest examples was described by Johnson (1925) and was called the 'healthy potato virus'. This apparent contradiction in terms was used to designate what is now universally known as 'potato virus X'; this virus was carried without visible symptoms by many of the American potato varieties.

As would perhaps be expected, chronic latent infection is commonest in plants which are vegetatively propagated.

No doubt the continual propagation of the virus in the same host helps to bring about a state of equilibrium between virus and host plant. In the case of potato virus X, 'virulence' or 'latency' are as much a function of the host plant as of the virus, since the same virus may be latent in one potato variety and virulent in another. This kind of reaction occurs with other plant viruses; a certain variety of dahlia, Bishop of Llandaff, for example, will carry the virus of cucumber mosaic without symptoms, while another dahlia variety will give a mosaic mottle and leaf distortion with the same virus. Certain varieties of the hop plant, notably Fuggles, have a latent infection with the hop mosaic virus, whereas on the Goldings hop the same virus is virulent. Latent infections are common also in raspberry and strawberry plants.

Good examples of latent infection, especially in weeds, are found among the soil-transmitted viruses of the tobacco ringspot group and also of the tobacco necrosis viruses.

*Economic Significance of Latent Virus Infections*

It is fairly obvious, if a virus-diseased plant is in the vicinity of a susceptible crop and if, as is probable, there exist one or more methods by which the virus can spread in the field, that the susceptible crop is likely to become virus-diseased. In such a case it is possible to take some remedial measures such as the elimination of the source of virus or the control of a potential vector. The situation becomes more serious when the source of virus is a latent infection, and here, of course, the first step is to locate the source, and this is not always easy. For example, it was some years before the serious disease of raspberry plants in Scotland, known as 'yellow dwarf', was found to be due to a soil-transmitted virus of the 'ringspot' type carried without symptoms by a number of common weeds (Cadman, 1960).

It is among fruit trees, and more especially stone fruits, that latent infections are of great economic importance. So often the root-stocks, used in grafting, harbour one or more latent infections, and thus large numbers of young trees become infected without the grower's knowledge.

Among stone-fruit trees, the peach X virus, the ringspot and ring mottle viruses in cherries, and the bark-split virus in plums may be mentioned. The rubbery wood virus is latent in many apple varieties and sooty ringspot virus in pears. Two other latent infections in pears, the viruses of yellow blotch and bark necrosis, have been recorded by Posnette and Cropley (1958).

One of the most serious cases of losses due to a virus infection which was latent in a fruit tree scion, but caused disease in the grafted stock, is the tristeza disease of citrus trees previously mentioned. For example, in 1946 in the principal citrus-producing state of São Paulo in Brazil, the virus was responsible for the loss of over 4 million trees. Up to 1937, the disease was not known in Brazil, but it was then recognized as identical with a 'root rot' responsible for very heavy damage in northern Argentina where it decimated the groves of sweet orange grafted on intolerant sour orange stocks. Originally known as a 'root rot' before its virus nature was recognized, the tristeza disease was first observed in South Africa about 1910, in Java in 1928, in Argentina about 1931, and in Brazil in 1937. It is also widespread in Israel and the U.S.A. Now, however, it is possible to take control measures, since it is known that the virus is latent in the sweet orange grafts and since the insect vectors, *Aphis citricidus* Kirk and *A. gossypii* Glover, have been identified. (See page 106).

## Resistance to Infection

As we have already seen in the discussion on virus interference, it is obvious that there exist many degrees of natural resistance in plants towards virus infection. This resistance may depend on the variety or species of host plant, on environmental conditions, and on the virus itself. Plant viruses are liable to changes which may be induced by long sojourn in one particular host, so that transfer to a new host species may make it difficult for the virus to readjust to new conditions. As we shall see in Chapter Eight, long continued transfer of an insect-transmitted virus by vegetative propagation of the host may cause it to lose its vector relationships. Holmes (1965) suggests three types of resistance: (a) degree of tolerance after infection; (b) level of susceptibility to infection; (c) decreased ease of recovery of virus from infected tissues. The first seems to imply an ability on the part of the host to reduce the rate of viral multiplication or to restrain the spread of virus through its tissues. The second, like the first, has unlimited variations. Some plants are easily infected by mechanical inoculation or by the feeding process of insects. Others can be infected by these methods, but with more difficulty, or by the feeding of specific insect vectors only. In the third case there is conspicuous necrosis in the infected plant, or the response may be the formation of local lesions only (see Chapter Ten), as with tobacco mosaic virus on the leaves of *Nicotiana glutinosa*. Here there is so little virus that spread of the disease is virtually eliminated.

Holmes (1965) lists a number of plant virus diseases for which single or multiple genes have been found to confer resistance, and a few of these are quoted here. Diachun and Henson (1959) found that tolerance to infection by bean yellow mosaic virus is controlled by a single dominant gene in crosses involving tolerant and mottling-type varieties of red clover (*Trifolium pratense* L.). In flowering stocks *Matthiola incana*), a high degree of resistance to turnip mosaic virus was found to be dependent on the presence of a single recessive gene, rm, in homozygous condition (Johnson and Barnhart, 1956).

The type of resistance shown by *Nicotiana glutinosa* to infection by tobacco mosaic virus, i.e. the local-lesion reaction, is controlled by a single dominant gene. This has now been incorporated into many locally satisfactory varieties of tobacco and has proved highly effective in preventing the spread of the virus in the field (Henderson *et al.*, 1957; Apple *et al.*, 1962).

In 1957, Isaacs and Lindeman reported the discovery of an antiviral substance produced by the cells of many vertebrates in response to virus infection. It appears to be of protein or polypeptide nature, it is antigenically distinct from virus, and it acts by conferring on cells resistance to the multiplication of a number of different viruses. The name given to this substance is 'Interferon', derived from the part it plays in virus interference (Isaacs, 1963).

This discovery stimulated inquiry as to whether some similar substance might not be produced by plant cells when invaded by viruses. There is in fact considerable evidence that some substance exists by which a plant can increase its resistance against further infection. Some early work on these lines was carried out by Wallace (1940, 1944) on the sugar-beet curly-top virus. He showed that tobacco and tomato plants grafted with scions from recovered plants produce no or few symptoms. This is not the case when transmission is made by insect vectors. Wallace suggested that specific substances are produced during infection which either inhibit virus multiplication or else bring about changes in the plants which enable them to tolerate the virus. These substances are able to pass through the graft but are not carried by the leafhopper vector.

Some work by Sela and Applebaum (1962) offers the first direct evidence that an 'antiviral factor' seems to appear during infection. Sap from different plants infected with potato virus Y or TMV was treated with hydrated calcium phosphate gel which adsorbs the virus. The supernatant fluid after centrifugation was not infective, but when mixed with potato virus Y or TMV it decreased the number of local lesions formed by these two viruses by amounts varying from 40 to 90 per cent. Controls were made with the same concentrations of virus mixed with sap from healthy plants treated with hydrated calcium phosphate in the same way. The antiviral factor was also isolated from the upper leaves of plants, the lower leaves of which were infected with a localized virus. The antiviral factor was retained in a dialysis sac and appeared to have no specific action. It does not seem to matter by which virus or on what plant the antiviral factor was produced; its actions were very similar on the two viruses and several plants on which it was tested (Kassanis, 1963).

A somewhat similar phenomenon can be observed when TMV is inoculated to *Nicotiana tabacum* var. *samsun* NN. This variety produces only local lesions on the inoculated leaves from which the virus does not spread. Nevertheless, resistance is induced to TMV on uninoculated opposite half-leaves or in leaves above or below those inoculated. The resistance is not specific and infection with TMV also makes leaves resistant to other viruses, such as those of tobacco necrosis, turnip mosaic, and ringspot (Ross and Bozarth, 1960; Ross, 1961).

According to Bozarth *et al.* (1962), no resistance was induced by mechanical or chemical injury of the leaves or by viruses which do not induce necrosis, but resistance was induced by the fungus *Thielaviopsis basicola* which produces lesions similar to those caused by tobacco necrosis virus. It seems therefore as if, in this instance, the resistance is tied up with the necrotic reaction rather than a virus infection.

Some further evidence is found in the work of Zaitlin and Siegel (1962) on the inhibition of tobacco mosaic virus infection by tobacco leaf cells. They were able to isolate a substance from incubated healthy tobacco cells that inhibited the TMV infection process.

Some more recent studies on an interferon-like substance in plants have been carried out by Loebenstein *et al.* (1966). It has been shown that resistance to virus infection can be induced by viral agents (TMV against TMV, virus against a non-related virus) and also by fungal agents. Attempts were therefore made to extract an interfering agent from the resistant tissue. Resistance was induced by inoculating the basal halves of *Datura stramonium* leaves with TMV or tobacco necrosis virus. The apical non-infected halves were used for extraction 7 to 10 days after inoculating the basal halves. The extracts were homogenized and centrifuged and the supernatant was tested against TMV for the presence of the interfering agent. Some properties of the agent were investigated; it could be destroyed by heating at 70°C for 15 minutes, but not by heating at 68°C for 15 minutes. Its activity is greatly reduced by incubation with trypsin; it is stable to dialysis and also to treatment with 2N perchloric acid. The agent does not inactivate virus *in vitro*; its interference is therefore probably via the host.

A similar interfering agent could also be induced by systemic infection of *D. stramonium* by potato virus X (PVX). Comparison of this agent with interferon reveals a number of similarities.

Atanasoff (1963) is of the opinion that the phenomena of 'acquired immunity', 'masked carriers', or 'interference' between viruses are all explainable by assuming the presence of interferon in plants.

# References

ATANASOFF, D. (1963) *Phytopathol. Z.* **47**, 207–14.

APPLE, J. L., CHAPLIN, J. F., and MANN, T. J. (1962) *Phytopathology.* **52**, 722 (Abstr.).

BAWDEN, F. C. (1958) *Sympos. Latency and Masking in Viral and Rickettsial Infections.* pp. 80–7. Minneapolis: Burgess Publ. Co.

BAWDEN, F. C. and KASSANIS, B. (1945) *Ann. appl. Biol.* **32**, 52–7.

BAWDEN, F. C. and KASSANIS, B. (1951) *Ann. appl. Biol.* **38**, 402–10.

BAWDEN, F. C. and PIRIE, N. W. (1937) *Brit. J. exp. Path.* **18**, 275–91.

BAWDEN, F. C. and SHEFFIELD, F. M. L. (1944) *Ann. appl. Biol.* **31**, 33–40.

BENNETT, C. W. (1927) *Mich. Agric. Exp. Sta. Tech. Bull.* No. 80.

BENNETT, C. W. (1944) *Phytopathology.* **34**, 77–91.

BENNETT, C. W. (1949) *Phytopathology.* **39**, 637–46.

BENNETT, C. W. (1953) *Adv. Vir. Res.* **1**, 40–67.

BENNETT, C. W. (1959) *Rep. Proc. 7th Internat. Congr. Microbiol.* 1958. Stockholm. pp. 218–23.

BENNETT, C. W. (1960) *U.S. Dept. Agr. Tech. Bull.* **1218**, 1–63.

BOZARTH, R. F., HECHT, EVA I., and ROSS, A. F. (1962) *Phytopathology.* **52**, 4 (Abstr.).

BUVAT, A. M. (1957) *Compt. Rend. Acad. Sci.* **245**, 198.

CADMAN, C. H. (1960) *Virology.* **11**, 653.

CALDWELL, J. (1930) *Ann. appl. Biol.* **17**, 429–43.

CALDWELL, J. (1934) *Ann. appl. Biol.* **21**, 206–24.

CLINCH, P. (1932) *Sci. Proc. Roy. Dublin Soc. N. S.* **20**, 143–72.

CLOSE, R. (1962) Ph.D. Thesis, Univ. of London. p. 144.

COOK, M. T. (1947) *Viruses and Virus Diseases of Plants.* Minneapolis: Burgess Publ. Co.

DIACHUN, S. and HENSON, L. (1959) *Phytopathology.* **49**, 537.

DIENER, T. O. (1963) *Ann. Rev. Phytopathology.* **1**, 197–218.

ESAU, K., CRONSHAW, J., and HOEFERT, L. L. (1967) *J. Cell Biol.* **32**, 71–87.

FULTON, R. W. (1950) *Phytopathology.* **40**, 219–20.

FULTON, R. W. (1951) *Phytopathology.* **41**, 578–92.

GARCES-OREJUELA, C. and POUND, G. S. (1957) *Phytopathology.* **47**, 232–9.

GIDDINGS, N. J. (1950) *Phytopathology.* **40**, 377–88.

HELMS, K. (1965) *Virology.* **27**, 346–50.

HENDERSON, R. D., SEARS, R. D., and SPASOFF, L. (1957) *Virginia J. Sci.* **8**, 267.

HOLMES, F. O. (1964) 'Symptomatology of viral diseases in plants'. *Plant Virology*, pp. 17–38. Eds. M. K. Corbett and H. D. Sisler. Gainesville: Univ. of Florida Press.

HOLMES, F. O. (1965) *Adv. Vir. Res.* **11**, 139–61.

HOUSTON, B. R., ESAU, K., and HEWITT, W. B. (1947) *Phytopathology.* **37**, 247–54.

HUTTON, E. M. (1948) *Austral. J. Sci. Res.* **B1**, 439–51.

ISAACS, A. (1963) *Adv. Vir. Res.* **10**, 1–38.

ISAACS, A. and LINDENMANN, J. (1957) *Proc. Roy. Soc. Ser. B.* **147**, 258.

JOHNSON, J. (1925) *Wisc. Agric. Exp. Sta. Res. Bull.* No. 63.

JOHNSON, B. L. and BARNHART, D. (1956) *Proc. Amer. Soc. Hort. Sci.* **67**, 522–33.

KASSANIS, B. (1957) *Ann. appl. Biol.* **45**, 422–7.

KASSANIS, B. (1963) *Adv. Vir. Res.* **10**, 219–55.

KASSANIS, B., TINSLEY, T. W., and QUAK, F. (1958) *Ann. appl. Biol.* **46**, 11–19.

KNIGHT, C. A. and STANLEY, W. M. (1941) *J. biol. Chem.* **141**, 39–49.

LOEBENSTEIN, G., RABINA, S., and VAN PRAAGH, T. (1966) in *Viruses of Plants.* pp. 151–7. Eds. A. B. R. Beemster and J. Dijkstra. Amsterdam: North Holland Publ. Co.

LIVINGSTON, L. G. (1964) *Amer. J. Bot.* **51**, 950.

LWOFF, A. (1958) *Sympos. Latency and Masking in Viral and Rickettsial Infections.* pp. 185–9. Minneapolis: Burgess Publ. Co.

MATTHEWS, R. E. F. (1949) *Nature, Lond.* **163**, 175.

MCKINNEY, H. H. (1929) *J. Agric. Res.* **39**, 557–78.

MCKINNEY, H. H. (1940) *Rep. Proc. 3rd Internat. Congr. Microbiol.* 1939. New York. p. 316.

MCKINNEY, H. H. (1941) *Amer. J. Bot.* **28**, 770–8.

MURPHY, P. A. and MCKAY, R. (1932) *Sci. Proc. Roy. Dublin. Soc. N. S.* **20**, 247–77.

OWEN, P. C. (1955a) *Ann. appl. Biol.* **43**, 114–21.

OWEN, P. C. (1955b) *Ann. appl. Biol.* **43**, 265–72.

OWEN, P. C. (1956) *Ann. appl. Biol.* **44**, 227–32.

OWEN, P. C. (1957) *Ann. appl. Biol.* **45**, 327–31.

POSNETTE, A. F. and CROPLEY, R. (1958) *J. hort. Sci.* **33**, 289–91.

PRICE, W. C. (1932) *Contr. Boyce Thompson Inst.* **4**, 359–403.

PRICE, W. C. (1939) *Phytopathology.* **29**, 903–5.

RAPPAPORT, I. and WILDMAN, S. G. (1957) *Virology.* **4**, 265.

'Recent Progress in Microbiology'. Symposium IV. Latent and Masked Virus Infections. *Rep. Proc. 7th. Internat. Congr. Microbiol.* 1958. Stockholm.

ROSS, A. F. (1950) *Phytopathology.* **40**, 445–52.

ROSS, A. F. (1959) in 'Plant Pathology – Problems and Progress, 1908–1958'. *Phytopathology.* Jubilee Vol. Symposia.

ROSS, A. F. (1961) *Virology.* **14,** 340.

ROSS, A. F. and BOZARTH, R. F. (1960) *Phytopathology.* **50,** 652.

SADASIVAN, T. S. (1940) *Ann. appl. Biol.* **27,** 359.

SALAMAN, R. N. (1933) *Nature. Lond.* **131,** 468.

SCHNEIDER, I. R. (1965) *Adv.⁊Vir. Res.* **11,** 163–221.

SELA, I. and APPLEBAUM, S. W. (1962) *Virology.* **17,** 543.

SHALLA, T. A. (1959) *Virology.* **7,** 193.

SHEFFIELD, F. M. L. (1933) *Ann. appl. Biol.* **20,** 57–69.

SIEGEL, A. (1959) *Virology.* **8,** 470.

SIEGEL, A., ZAITLIN, M., and SEHGAL, O. P. (1962) *Proc. Natl. Acad. Sci. U.S.* **48,** 1845.

SMITH, K. M. (1931) *Proc. Roy. Soc. B.* **109,** 251.

SMITH, K. M. (1933) *Biol Rev.* **8,** 136–79.

SMITH, K. M. (1935) *Parasitology.* **27,** 450–60.

SMITH, K. M. (1946) *Parasitology.* **37,** 126–30.

SMITH, K. M. (1952) *Biol. Rev.* **27,** 347–57.

SMITH, K. M. (1967) *Insect Virology.* p. 150. New York: Academic Press. *Symposium on Latency and Masking in Viral and Rickettsial Infections.* 1958. Minneapolis: Burgess Publ. Co.

TALL, M. G., PRICE, W. C., and WESTMAN, K. (1949) *Phytopathology.* **39,** 288–9.

THOMSON, A. D. (1960) *Nature.* **187,** 761.

THUNG, T. H. (1931) *Handelingen 6 de Nederle-Inde. Naturwetensch. Cong.* 450–63.

WALLACE, J. M. (1940) *Phytopathology.* **30,** 673.

WALLACE, J. M. (1944) *J. Agr. Res.* **69,** 187.

WHITEHEAD, T. (1934) *Ann. appl. Biol.* **21,** 48–77.

WU, J. H. and RAPPAPORT, I. (1961) *Virology.* **14,** 259.

ZAITLIN, M. and SIEGEL, A. (1962) *Phytopathology.* **52,** 367.

ZECH, H. and VOGT-KÖHNE, L. (1956) *Exptl. Cell Res.* **10,** 458.

# CHAPTER FOUR

# Isolation and Purification of Plant Viruses

---

When investigating a possibly undescribed sap-transmissible virus, it is desirable to have some information on certain elementary properties of the virus before commencing more comprehensive studies on its purification. What is wanted is some information on its stability and concentration in the plant, because attempts at isolation are likely to be much more difficult if the virus in question is extremely labile or occurs in very low concentration. The three elementary tests usually carried out are to determine: (*a*) the ageing, or longevity *in vitro*, of the virus in extracted sap; (*b*) the thermal inactivation point; and (*c*) the dilution end-point.

It should be realized that the results of these tests are likely to be approximate only, since much may depend on the source of the virus, the availability of a good indicator host or assay plant, and other factors. In making the tests there are several conventions which should be followed, and there must be a preliminary clarification of the virus-containing sap, because the presence of whole cells would obviously vitiate the results. The sap is expressed from the sample infected plant usually with a pestle and mortar and filtered through a piece of fine muslin or cheese cloth; it should then be clarified by low-speed centrifugation.

## Elementary Tests
*Longevity* in vitro
The clarified sap is placed in a small conical flask and kept in the laboratory at room temperature. Inoculations are made at intervals to an appropriate test plant. At first the test may be made every 24 hours, but this interval can, of course, be increased if the infectivity seems likely to last for weeks or longer.

*Dilution End-point*

Using clarified sap, a number of dilutions are made, a fresh pipette being employed for each dilution. Beginning with a dilution of 1:10, the series is usually carried to 1:1,000,000, but infections are likely to cease considerably before that. If they cease at 1:100, purification will probably be a difficult problem.

*Thermal Inactivation Point*

The conventions here are to use a thin-walled test-tube to hold the clarified sap and to give an exposure of 10 minutes to a range of temperatures. The bulb of the thermometer is immersed in the sap, the test-tube is placed in a water-bath and held at the required temperature for 10 minutes. The test-tube is then cooled under the tap and inoculations are made to the indicator plants. The usual range of temperatures tested is 45 to 80°C in 5-degree steps. It will be found that plant viruses vary in their thermal inactivation point, but the majority are between 50 and 60°C.

**Purification Methods**

The problems involved in separating a virus from the plant cell constituents are numerous and are only partially solved. Only a small percentage of the large number of sap-transmissible viruses known have been successfully purified. There are several points of practical importance to be considered before the purification of a virus can be accomplished. First, it is important that the virus should be present in sufficient concentration to make the attempt worthwhile; some information on this point can be obtained with the dilution end-point test described above. Markham (1959) considers that the minimum quantity of virus necessary is of the order of 5 to 10 mg of dry virus per kilogramme of fresh leaf material, but for consistently successful purification a larger quantity than this is desirable. Another important point is the plant used as a source of virus; many factors are concerned here. As a rule, young plants, showing recent systemic symptoms, have a higher virus content than old plants long infected, and contain less pigment. This is not an invariable rule, however, since turnip yellow mosaic virus occurs in higher concentration in old, hard, long-infected plants of Chinese cabbage or turnip than in young sappy plants recently infected.

Some plants are unsuitable for use as sources of virus; for example, those that contain large quantities of gums, latex, or tarry materials. Certain plants, such as New Zealand spinach (*Tetragonia expansa*), which contain inhibitors, are also to be avoided, as are strawberry plants because of their associated tannins.

It is important to have a susceptible, quickly reacting plant species available for use as an indicator plant or assay host, in order to test out the virus content at various stages of the purification process. One that reacts with local lesions on the inoculated leaves is best for this purpose (see Chapter Ten).

There are three main steps in the purification of a plant virus: (*a*) extraction of the sap; (*b*) clarification of the crude sap; (*c*) isolation of the virus. To extract the sap, the diseased plants should be minced; a domestic meat grinder with a worm which compresses the material before it reaches the cutters is most satisfactory. The extraction of the sap is helped if the leaves are frozen at about −10°C; they should be stored in polythene bags and not be allowed to dry. The leaf tissue is then thawed and minced; the wet pulp is pressed by hand through muslin and the sap is collected. Next the pulp residue is put in a hand or hydraulic press and the remainder of the sap is collected.

The next step is the clarification of the crude sap, and this can be done in several ways.

(1) Low-speed centrifugation, 10 to 30 minutes at 3,000 to 10,000$g$, removes most particles larger than the virus.

(2) Another method is filtration through filter paper or fritted glass filters.

(3) Heating or freezing may be used, provided this treatment does not affect the infectivity of the virus. This causes the denaturation and aggregation of some of the plant proteins which can then be removed by low-speed centrifugation.

(4) Filtration through charcoal, bentonite, diatomaceous earth, celite, etc. – these filter aids remove, besides the larger components, many of the small components other than virus (Steere, 1964).

Some of these filtration methods would not be suitable for certain viruses, potato virus Y for example adsorbs strongly to filter paper or kieselguhr. Corbett (1961) quoted by Steere (1964) describes a simple procedure which involved the addition of 5 g of activated charcoal per

100 ml of crude extract. The mixture is shaken for $\frac{1}{2}$ minute and then 5 g of diatomaceous earth, celite, or High Flow Super Cell is added. Shaking is continued for another $\frac{1}{2}$ minute and the mixture is poured on to a $\frac{1}{4}$-inch pad of the same diatomaceous earth in a Buchner funnel. If the diatomaceous earth is not added to the mixture, a thick layer of the large contaminants will soon cover the top of the filter cake and prevent or slow down the filtration of the remaining suspension. This method has its dangers because of the liability of the virus to adsorb to and be lost in the filter pad. It is important to try changes in buffer to avoid this contingency. With tobacco mosaic virus it is necessary to use buffers of pH 7.5 or higher to prevent adsorption of the virus to the pad of diatomaceous earth.

Another method of sap clarification is by the addition of organic solvents, Markham (1959) describes the use of ethanol. This involves the addition of 300 ml of 90 per cent ethanol to each litre of strained sap, with vigorous stirring. This procedure causes the immediate formation of a coagulum which may be centrifuged off at low speed, leaving a golden, slightly cloudy fluid which contains the virus. There are two possible drawbacks to this method, one is that there may be viruses which cannot tolerate this level of ethanol; the other is that the virus may be precipitated by weak ethanol at the pH of the sap.

The third step in the purification process is the isolation of the virus itself, and there are several techniques available to achieve this.

(1) *Precipitation of the Virus.* The two precipitating agents most commonly used are alcohol and ammonium sulphate. The alcohol can be used for precipitating either the virus or, as we have already seen, the extraneous plant proteins according to the particular virus being used or the strength of the alcohol. The amount of ammonium sulphate used is usually one third saturation.

(2) *Gel Filtration.* By this method the virus suspension is allowed to percolate slowly down a long tube filled with agar or 'Sephadex'. Very small particles enter the pores of the agar granules, but larger ones such as virus particles are unable to do this and will flow down through the column around and between the gel granules with the movement of liquid through the column. The virus thus arrives at the base of the column and can be collected before the arrival of the pigment and other small particles. For a full account of this technique see Steere (1964).

(3) *Ultracentrifugation.* This involves alternate cycles of high- and low-speed centrifugation; the pellet from the high-speed centrifugation is resuspended and then spun at a low speed to remove any large particles.

Some viruses cannot be purified by chemical precipitation methods either because they are too unstable or occur in too small concentration within the plant. In such cases, ultracentrifugation is employed and was used by Stanley (1939) to isolate the virus of tobacco ringspot. Steere (1956) re-examined the purification of this virus using Caserta squash (*Cucurbita pepo*) and petunia as propagation hosts instead of the more usual tobacco plant.

A refinement of the ultracentrifugation technique has been developed by Brakke (1951, 1960) and is known as 'density gradient centrifugation'. This consists of a sucrose density gradient in a centrifuge tube with the virus suspension layered on top of the gradient. The tubes are then placed in the centrifuge with a swinging bucket head which allows the tubes to swing out in a horizontal position. As the centrifuge slows down the tubes regain the perpendicular, so that the gradient remains undisturbed. This process separates out particles with differing densities into separate layers; the solution reaches a condition of equilibrium where the particles are unable to move farther down the tube. The successive layers can then be drawn off for testing for the presence of virus either from the top of the tube or, by using a plastic centrifuge tube, the layers can be drawn off through the side by using a hypodermic needle. A further refinement of this technique is the substitution of cesium chloride for sucrose (Miselson, Stahl, and Vinograd, 1957; Miselson and Stahl, 1958). Instead of layering the virus on top of the gradient, it is mixed with the salt in the centrifuge tube and a gradient is established during centrifugation. The various particles in the solution will find their own density level and thus arrange themselves in layers which can be separately removed.

In order to make some of these various purification procedures clearer to the reader, the purification of a few viruses will be briefly described, starting with turnip yellow mosaic virus. This is one of the easiest plant viruses to isolate (Markham and K. M. Smith, 1949).

The best source plants are Chinese cabbage or turnips, the former grow better under glass and the virus content is higher in old pot-bound

D

plants than in those which are young and sappy. The plants should be harvested about 2 months after infection and then ground up and the sap expressed.

The sap is clarified by the addition of 300 ml of 90 per cent ethanol to each litre of sap, the flocculent precipitate of plant proteins is spun off, and the supernatant liquid, which is yellow and slightly opalescent, has a half-volume of saturated ammonium sulphate in water added. Crystallization of the virus begins in a few minutes, and is complete in 4 or 5 hours. At the same time, strongly birefringent crystals, possibly of calcium sulphate, are also found, but these are insoluble in water, so that the pellet of crystals obtained on centrifuging may be extracted with water and reprecipitated as crystals. Under normal conditions, three or four recrystallizations of the virus from ammonium sulphate suffice for the purification. Crystallization follows smoothly after enough salt has been added to make the solution slightly cloudy, and it is virtually impossible to prepare the virus in an amorphous state. The crystals are octahedra when purified by this method.

Turnip yellow mosaic virus is a very small icosahedron; it will be of interest now to investigate the purification of some larger viruses.

For purification of lucerne (alfalfa) mosaic virus, the sap was extracted from the young leaves of tobacco plants 10 to 14 days after they had been inoculated. The leaves were macerated mechanically at $0°C$ in an equal weight of pH 7 buffer made by mixing equal volumes of 0.2 M disodium hydrogen phosphate and 0.1 M ascorbic acid. Chloroform (half the volume of the buffer) was then added and the mixture was macerated further to form an emulsion. The emulsion was centrifuged at $3000g$ for 10 minutes, and the aqueous extract was removed, stored overnight at room temperature, and centrifuged again at $3000g$ for 10 minutes. Then the extract was centrifuged at $75,000g$ for 2 hours at $4°C$ and the virus-containing pellet was suspended in 0·01 M ammonium acetate at pH 7 and finally centrifuged at $8000g$ for 10 minutes. Purified preparations were fractionated by rate zonal centrifugation in sucrose density gradients (Gibbs, Nixon, and Woods, 1963).

Tomato spotted wilt virus is reversibly aggregated by 0·1 M potassium phosphate. It was partly purified by grinding diseased plants with 0·1 M, pH 7 potassium phosphate buffer, centrifuging the extract at low speed and resuspending the pellet in 0·01 M $Na_2SO_3$, in which the virus was dispersed. The virus solution was then given one cycle of differential centrifugation and one of density gradient centrifugation. It was important to use source plants at a stage of the disease at which they contained a peak concentration of the virus (Black, Brakke, and Vatter, 1963).

A common aphid-transmitted virus which is rather difficult to purify is that of cucumber mosaic. There have been several attempts to isolate this virus (Tomlinson *et al.*, 1959) and the most recent is given here (Scott, 1963). He used tobacco tissue infected with the Y strain of cucumber mosaic virus (CMV-Y) which was extracted with a mixture of chloroform and 0·5 M citrate or phosphate buffer. Dialysis of the aqueous phase against 0·005 M borate buffer, pH 9, followed by three cycles of differential centrifugation, resulted in active preparations which had a typical nucleoprotein spectrum, contained polyhedral particles of 28·30 mμ diameter, and showed a major and a minor component in the analytical centrifuge. The detailed procedure was as follows, and was carried out at 0 to 4°C.

(1) Infected tissue (300 to 600 g) is homogenized in 0·5 M citrate buffer, pH 6·5 (containing 0·1 per cent thioglycolic acid), and chloroform in proportions of 1 g: 1 ml respectively.

(2) The emulsion is broken down by centrifuging at 1200g for 10 minutes.

(3) The aqueous phase is dialyzed against 0·005 M borate buffer pH 9, (30 to 40 ml of dialysing buffer per millilitre of virus extract) for 20 to 24 hours.

(4) The dialyzate is centrifuged at 54,000g for 15 minutes.

(5) The clarified dialyzate in centrifuged for 150 minutes at 78,000g.

(6) Pellets are resuspended in 0·005 M borate buffer, pH 9, and the suspension is clarified at 5,400g for 15 minutes to remove insoluble materials and aggregates.

(7) The clarified suspension is recentrifuged for 90 minutes at 105,000g, pellets are resuspended in the same borate buffer and clarified as before.

(8) Procedure number 7 is repeated.

A new method of isolation which has some advantages over the methods just given has been suggested by Leberman (1966) and his technique is briefly described. He employs *coacervation* which implies the separation of a macromolecular solution into two liquid layers, one poor in colloid and the other rich in it.

The sap is extracted from infected plants by the usual method of mincing, straining, and pressing the leaves. It is then clarified by centrifugation at 12,000$g$ for 30 minutes. For each 100 ml of clarified sap are added 1·34 g of sodium dextran sulphate (DS) in a 20 per cent solution, 29 g of polyethylene glycol (PEG) in a 30 per cent solution, and 5 g of 5M NaCl. The resultant mixture is poured into large separating funnels and left to separate in a cold room at 4°C overnight. The lower phase and interface are collected and centrifuged at low speed. The pellet consists of the lower phase covered with particulate matter which collects at the interface; the supernatant is upper phase and is discarded. To extract the virus from the pellet, potassium chloride is added to precipitate the DS as the potassium salt, 0·2 ml of 3M KCl per gramme of the original amount of DS solution being sufficient. In practice, however, 3M KCl is added with stirring until a thin creamy paste is obtained. This is centrifuged at low speed to remove potassium DS and most of the material from the interface. Further extractions of the pellet can be carried out with 0·5M KCl. The combined extracts are then centrifuged in a No 30 rotor of Spinco model L at 30,000 rpm for 2½ hours. The pellets are resuspended in 0·1 M ethylenediaminetetra-acetic acid (EDTA), pH 7 (Na$_2$EDTA$_r$adjusted to pH 7 with NaOH); EDTA is used at this point to dissociate any ribosomes that may have been present. The virus can then be further purified by one or two cycles of high- and low-speed centrifugation, the virus pellet being suspended in any desired buffer or salt medium.

Details of the morphology and ultrastructure of viruses isolated by some of the foregoing methods are given in the next chapter.

## References

BRAKKE, M. K. (1951) *J. Amer. Chem. Soc.* **73**, 1847.

BRAKKE, M. K. (1960) *Adv. Vir. Res.* **7**, 193.

BLACK, L. M., BRAKKE, M. K., and VATTER, A. E. (1963) *Virology.* **20**, 120–30.

CORBETT, M. K. (1961) *Virology.* **15**, 8.

GIBBS, A. J., NIXON, H. L., and WOODS, R. D. (1963) *Virology.* **19**, 441–9.

LEBERMAN, R. (1966) *Virology.* **30**, 341–7.

MARKHAM, R. (1959) 'Plant and Bacterial Viruses'. *The Viruses.* Vol. 2. Eds. F. M. Burnet and W. M. Stanley. New York: Academic Press.

MARKHAM, R. and SMITH, K. M. (1949) *Parasitology.* **39**, 330–42.

MISELSON, M. and STAHL, F. W. (1958) *Proc. Nat. Acad. Sci. U.S.A.* **44**, 671.

MISELSON, M., STAHL, F. W., and VINOGRAD, J. (1957) *Proc. Nat. Acad. Sci. U.S.A.* **43**, 581.

SCOTT, H. (1963) *Virology.* **20**, 103.

STANLEY, W. M. (1939) *J. biol. Chem.* **129**, 405–28.

STEERE, R. L. (1956) *Phytopathology.* **46**, 60–9.

STEERE, R. L. (1964) in *Plant Virology.* pp. 211–34. Eds. M. K. Corbett and H. D. Sisler. Gainesville: Univ. of Florida Press.

TOMLINSON, J. A., SHEPHERD, R. J., and WALKER, J. C. (1959) *Phytopathology.* **49**, 293–9.

# CHAPTER FIVE

# Morphology and Ultrastructure of the Virus Particles. Plant Viruses *in situ* in Plant and Insect Vector

## Morphology and Ultrastructure of the Virus Particles

In essence, a plant virus particle consists of a strand of ribonucleic acid (RNA) surrounded by a protein coat, the purpose of which is to afford a protective covering for the nucleic acid. The nomenclature suggested for the particle and its components is as follows: the whole particle is called a 'virion', the protein coat is the 'capsid' and the individual protein subunits are known as 'capsomeres'. The structure composed of the nucleic acid surrounded by the capsid is the 'nucleocapsid'. Essentially, all viruses seem to have their outside surfaces composed of regularly arranged protein units, with their nucleic acid carried internally. The type of pattern in which the protein units are arranged differs with different viruses, as also must the position and orientation of the nucleic acid relative to the protein covering (Bawden, 1964).

The shapes of plant virus particles fall into two general categories, the *anisometric* and the *isometric* particles. The first group can be subdivided into bacillus-like bodies, only a few times longer than broad – included here are the bullet-shaped viruses (Hitchborn *et al.*, 1966) and the large virus of lettuce necrotic yellows (Harrison and Crowley, 1965) – and into rigid rods and long flexible threads.

The isometric particles, which are a crystalline form that has three equal axes at right-angles to one another, appear spherical but are actually polyhedral. Crick and Watson (1956) pointed out that only regular bonding of identical units using one of three types of cubic symmetry, tetrahedral, octahedral, or icosahedral, was likely to lead to an isometric particle. It has now been shown that the small plant viruses are icosahedra, a figure with twenty sides. The design of these particles will be discussed later.

*Anisometric Viruses*

Among the viruses with anisometric particles, those which are rod-shaped are the most common. They vary in appearance from the rigid type to long flexuous rods. An attempt to classify these viruses, based on their lengths and diameters, has been made by Brandes and Bercks (1965), and the following measurements are quoted from their publication. There are two groups of viruses with short rigid rods, the tobacco rattle virus group with diameters of 20 to 22 m$\mu$ and lengths of 130 to 180 m$\mu$, and the tobacco mosaic virus group with diameters of about 18 m$\mu$ and lengths of 300 to 315 m$\mu$.

The potato virus X group contains long flexible particles about 13 m$\mu$ in diameter and 480 to 580 m$\mu$ in length.

The potato virus S group has particles which may be described as being rigid to slightly flexible and are often curved to one side. They have a diameter of about 15 m$\mu$ and lengths of 620 to 700 m$\mu$. Viruses of the potato virus Y group have flexible particles and lengths of 730 to 790 m$\mu$.

One of two elongated viruses have different morphological characteristics from any of the foregoing. The virus of beet yellows has very long flexible particles, measuring 1250 m$\mu$ in length and about 10 m$\mu$ in diameter (Brandes and Zimmer, 1955). Other very long particles are those of a virus from *Festuca* (Schmidt *et al.*, 1963) and citrus tristeza disease (Kitajima *et al.*, 1963). Of all the rod-shaped viruses, that of tobacco mosaic has been the most studied so that an account of its ultrastructure will be given in some detail.

*The Tobacco Mosaic Virus Particle* (TMV). Although much of our knowledge of the fine structure of the tobacco mosaic virus particle comes from X-ray diffraction studies, investigation by other methods showed that the particle was not just a solid rod. Degradation by alkali revealed the presence of threads joining segments of rods or protruding from the ends (Schramm, Schumacher, and Zillig, 1955). Hart (1955) removed part of the protein coat of the virus rod by treatment with sodium dodecyl sulphate; this revealed an axial thread. He confirmed that this was the ribonucleic acid (RNA) since treatment with the enzyme ribonuclease removed it, but treatment with deoxyribonuclease or trypsin had no effect. Hart also suggested that the two ends of the rod might not be identical since the nucleic acid protruded from only one end. See also tobacco rattle virus in this respect. Huxley (1957), by negative staining, confirmed the presence of a central hole in the rod.

X-ray diffraction studies (Klug and Caspar, 1960) on the TMV particle have shown that it consists of a helical array of protein subunits of pitch 23 Å, containing a single chain of RNA which follows the same basic helix at a radius of 40 Å. There are 49 protein subunits in three turns of the helix. The virus particle has a hole of diameter 40 Å extending along the axis and the cylindrically averaged diameter of the particle is close to 150 Å (Finch, 1964).

Electron micrographs show the virus as rod-shaped, about 150 Å in diameter with a length of 3,000 Å (Williams and Steere, 1951; Hall, 1958). Until recently, attempts to visualize the helical nature of the virus rod by electron microscopy have been disappointing, although Nixon and Woods (1960) observed cross-striations on particles of repolymerized TMV protein. They considered that the spacing of the transverse bands corresponded to that of individual turns of the protein helix.

However, Finch (1964) has now published electron micrographs of lengths of TMV particles negatively stained with uranyl formate; in these the 23-Å pitch of the basic helix is clearly visible in many places right across the particle and in others as a serration on the edge of the particle. The micrographs of a fairly uniform preparation of TMV negatively stained with uranyl formate show a predominant length close to 3,000 Å, the same particles showing a pitch of 23 Å. The number of turns in a complete virus particle is therefore about 130.

*Potato Virus X.* The particle of this virus is somewhat similar to TMV, but is longer and less rigid. The structure is helical with a pitch close to that of TMV, but the subunit packing repeats after two instead of three turns (Klug and Caspar, 1960).

*Sugar-beet Yellows Virus.* This is a sinuous filamentous structure about 100 Å in diameter and over a micron in length. The particles have a central hollow core of diameter 30 to 40 Å, and a regular periodicity along their length of about 20 to 30 Å. By analogy with TMV, it therefore seems very likely that the virus has a loose, hollow, helical structure with a pitch slightly greater than that of TMV (Horne *et al.*, 1959).

*Tobacco Rattle Virus*. In this case the particle is rod-shaped but more rigid than TMV. It is tubular with a central hole approximately 4 mμ in diameter with a width between 17 and 25 mμ (Nixon and Harrison, 1959) (Plate 4).

Out of ten tobacco rattle virus samples from Europe and America, all had straight tubular particles of two or more different lengths, each length being characteristic of the virus isolate. Only the longest particles were infective. The two ends of individual particles differed, the axial canal being flared at one end (Harrison and Woods, 1966).

Several viruses which are bullet-shaped or bacilliform have been isolated and brief descriptions of their morphology are given.

*Lucerne (Alfalfa) Mosaic Virus*. Purified preparations of this virus contain bacilliform particles, which, mounted in neutral phosphotungstic acid, are 18 mμ wide and of various lengths though mostly 36, 48, and 58 mμ long (Plate 5). Particles of all sizes contained about 17 per cent ribonucleic acid and were serologically and electrophoretically indistinguishable. All seemed equally infective except particles measuring 20 to 30 mμ which occurred in old preparations.

Negatively stained preparations showed evenly spaced knobs protruding from the surface of the particles (Gibbs *et al.*, 1963) (Plate 6).

Similar knobs have been described on the surface of the particles of *Gomphrena* virus which is thought to be related to the virus of lettuce necrotic yellows (Kitajima and Costa, 1966).

*Lettuce Necrotic Yellows Virus*. There seem to be particles of several different types associated with lettuce necrotic yellows, but these may be debris or aggregates of the infective particle which is bacilliform or bullet-shaped. When treated with uranyl acetate or uranyl formate, the particles appear to have an outer coat loosely enclosing a tubular inner body showing cross-banding at intervals of 4 to 5 mμ. The particle-size is 66 mμ wide by about 227 mμ long. This is one of the largest plant

viruses known and resembles in many respects the virus of bovine
vesicular stomatitis (Harrison and Crowley, 1965).

*Isometric Viruses*

Many of the small plant viruses, notably those of turnip yellow mosaic,
tomato bushy stunt, tobacco ringspot, tobacco necrosis, and others,
appear at first sight to be spherical when viewed in the electron microscope. However, while examining frozen-dried particles of squash
mosaic and turnip yellow mosaic viruses, Stahman and Kaesberg (1955)
noticed that they seemed to have a hexagonal contour. Kaesberg (1956)
investigated this matter further and examined in the electron microscope lightly shadowed, frozen-dried preparations of purified turnip
yellow mosaic, squash mosaic, wild cucumber mosaic (*Echinocystis
lobata*) and brome grass mosaic viruses. All these viruses suggested a
polygonal contour.

The first unequivocal evidence that the isometric viruses were icosahedra, with twenty sides, was provided by Williams and Smith (1958)
using an insect virus, the *Tipula* iridescent virus. The frozen-dried
virus particles were metal-shadowed from two angles; by this 'double-
shadow' method two shadows were thrown, and, when viewed in the
electron microscope, were seen to have pointed and blunt ends respectively. Such shadows are characteristic of an isosahedron. A similar
experiment carried out by Bils and Hall (1962) showed that a small
plant virus, that of wound tumour, gave similar shadow and was therefore also an icosahedron.

Steere (1957) developed a technique by which preshadowed replicas
can be obtained from plant virus crystals which have been cut and then
etched by sublimation of the ice from their surfaces. Electron micrographs of specimens prepared by this low-temperature replica procedure show that, in a crystal of tobacco ringspot virus in 0·01 M phosphate buffer, the individual virus particles show a hexagonal outline and
hexagonal packing within the crystal.

Chiefly because of the difficulties inherent in their small size, less
information has been obtained on the ultrastructure of the isometric
plant viruses and the exact relationships of protein and nucleic acid.
Studies by Markham and Smith (1949) and by Markham (1951) showed
that the sap of plants infected with turnip yellow mosaic contained two

components: one, the top component, consists only of a protein shell, and the other, the bottom component, is infectious and contains RNA within the protein shell. This work suggested that the small isometric plant viruses consisted of a protein shell containing nucleic acid, but more information is needed on the exact position of the nucleic acid *vis-à-vis* the protein. A flexible RNA molecule could be rolled up like a ball of string inside the shell, but the limited X-ray evidence (Klug and Finch, 1960) indicates that the RNA-folding is in fact related to the structure of the capsid, though it is not as highly organized as the protein-packing (Caspar, 1964). X-ray diffraction studies have shown that the small viruses of turnip yellow mosaic, tomato bushy stunt, and southern bean mosaic are all icosahedra (Klug and Finch, 1960 a and b).

Much work has been carried out on the ultrastructure of the particle of turnip yellow mosaic virus and the position of the RNA. The following information is taken from two recent papers by Finch and Klug (1966) and by Klug *et al.* (1966).

Earlier X-ray studies and also electron microscopy (Nixon and Gibbs, 1960; Huxley and Zubay, 1960) have shown that the protein shell of TYM has a surface structure of 32 knobs, these are known as 'morphological units'. X-ray diffraction studies have now shown that there are actually 180 units, called 'structural units'. The arrangement of these units is fairly uniform with no clumping into hexameters and pentameters. In the images of the virus particles, there is additional density linking the centres of the units into the 32 large morphological units. This additional density is absent in the top component which, as already stated, contains no RNA. Finch and Klug attribute this difference in appearance to the presence of RNA in the virus particles, so that the RNA must be distributed in such a way that local concentrations occur in the regions of the 32 surface lattice points. Photographs from crystals with a well-defined lattice show that the gross distribution of the RNA has the same icosahedral symmetry as the protein. A significant proportion of the RNA is deeply embedded within the protein shell, and the mode of winding of the single RNA chain must be such that large segments of it are intimately associated with the rings of 6 and 5 protein structure units which make up the protein shell. It is the presence of the RNA in and about these positions that enhances the appearance of 32 morphological units in the electron micrographs (see Fig. 1).

FIG. 1. Schematic drawing to indicate the relation of the gross RNA distribution in the turnip yellow mosaic virus particle to the arrangement of protein subunits. A section through a diametral plane of the virus particle is shown. The precise shape of the protein subunits and the detailed path of the RNA chain are not known, and neither is the distribution of protein and RNA towards the centre of the particle. (A. Klug, W. Longley, and R. Leberman, 1966.)

DLDC

FIG. 2. A drawing of the outer surface of the turnip yellow mosaic virus particle as revealed by negative staining (approximately × 2 million). The 180 structure units protrude about 20 Å from the main body of the particle, but their exact shape is not known. They are tilted somewhat out of the radial direction towards the directions of the three- and fivefold axes of the particle (although the clustering is not obvious in end-on views in negative-stain images, because the centres of contrast of the units lie below the outermost surface). The RNA is associated closely with the hexamers and pentamers at an inner radius (see Fig. 1). (D. L. D. Caspar in J. T. Finch and A. Klug, 1966.)

A drawing of the TYMV particle by D. L. D. Caspar is shown in Fig. 2. The 180 structure units protrude about 20 Å from the main body of the particle, but their exact shape is not known. They are tilted somewhat out of the radial direction towards the directions of the three- and five fold axes of the particle.

In Plate 7 is a micrograph of another isometric virus, that of cowpea chlorotic mottle, multiplied 2 million times. The picture was made by the photographic rotation technique (Markham *et al.* 1963).

## Plant Viruses *in situ* in Plant and Insect Vector
Until fairly recently there was little information on plant viruses *in situ* either in plant or in insect, and this was mainly concerned with tobacco mosaic virus. However, with the improvements in fixation and staining techniques for electron microscopy, much more attention has been paid to this aspect and, within the last two years, a dozen or more papers have been published dealing with the histopathology of virus-infected cells of both plants and insects. This type of work is valuable not only from the point of view of cell-virus relationships, but also because it may give more information on the cell organelles themselves by the close association of viruses with the endoplasmic reticulum, mitochondria, and golgi apparatus.

### Anisometric Viruses
Because of their distinctive shape which differentiates them sharply from the normal cell contents, it is fairly easy to visualize the rod-shaped viruses in the plant cell. This is particularly true of tobacco mosaic virus which can easily be seen in fibrous masses of regular particle arrangement (Edwardson 1966; Milne 1966) (Plate 8).

Associated with the longer and more flexible rods of the potato virus Y group, there occur in the cells numerous peculiar intracelluar inclusions shaped like 'pinwheels', cat-o-nine-tails, etc. (Plate 2) (Edwardson, 1966; Arnott and Smith, 1967). The consensus of opinion is that these inclusions consist of the viruses themselves but this is not proved. The virus masses seem to be restricted to the cytoplasm and, while not apparently associated directly with the nucleus, in the case of the sunflower virus (Arnott and Smith *loc. cit.*) there are marked changes in the nucleus and the plastids. Moreover there seems to be a direct association between the intracellular inclusions and the endoplasmic reticulum (Plate 2).

In leaves of *Nicotiana glutinosa* and *Lactuca sativa* infected with lettuce necrotic yellows virus, thick rod-shaped particles developed in the cytoplasm, and, were not encountered in the nucleus, mitochondria or chloroplasts (Plate 9). The virus particles usually occurred in bundles enclosed in double membranous structures, and the inner membranes of these structures are thought to be associated with the assembly of the virus particles (Chambers *et al.*, 1965).

Lettuce necrotic yellows virus has also been observed in the xylem tissue of *N. glutinosa*. The virus rods occur in bundles in a membrane and do not appear to be associated with any cytoplasmic organelle. The xylem cells containing the virus were immature tracheids or vessel elements (Chambers and Francki, 1966).

In a recent paper by Cronshaw *et al.* (1966) on the virus of sugar-beet yellows in the cells of infected plants, inclusions of particles of the size of beet yellows virus have been observed in the ground cytoplasm, in the chloroplasts, and in the nuclei. The observation of particles in the chloroplasts is of interest in view of the yellowing symptoms of the disease, and of the possibility that the replicating machinery of the plastids is being used by the virus.

So far as the visualization of anisometric viruses inside the insect vector is concerned, there is less information on this point than there is on the isometric viruses. Kikumoto and Matsui (1962) have demonstrated TMV inside the gut of aphids which had fed upon mosaic plants, but aphids are unable to transmit this virus (see Chapter 8).

*Isometric Viruses*

Because of their size and similarity to some normal cell contents, it is not easy to visualize the small isometric viruses within the plant cell. However, Smith (1956) demonstrated microcrystals of tomato bushy stunt virus in the cells of infected *Datura stramonium*.

The situation is rather different with the large leafhopper-borne viruses and quite a number have been visualized in both plant and insect vector.

Spherical particles, about 300 to 350 Å in diameter, and presumed to be the virus of pea enation mosaic, have been found in the cytoplasm, central vacuole, and nucleus of infected pea plants (Shikata and Mara-morosch, 1965, 1966).

The rather large particles of tomato spotted wilt virus (TSWV) have been observed in the root cells of infected tomato plants and in the leaf cells of *Tropaeolum majus* (Ie, 1964). Kitajima (1965), also working with TSWV, found intracellular virus particles in the leaves and root tissue cells of *Nicotiana tabacum*. These particles measure about 1,000 Å in diameter and consist of an outer membrane and internal dense dots. Kitajima considers that the constant association of the virus particles with the endoplasmic reticulum suggests that the latter is concerned in virus formation. He also thinks that the virus particles are too large to pass via the plasmodesmata and it is thought that this must be accomplished by some smaller precursor.

Herold *et al.* (1960) have demonstrated particles of a virus, probably that of maize (corn) mosaic, *in situ* in cells of infected maize. They occur in the cytoplasm around the nucleus and are often arranged in a regular three-dimensional order forming microcrystals. The particles are very regular in size and shape, measuring 242 mμ in length and 48 mμ in diameter. They have a highly differentiated structure with two limiting membranes and a dense rod-shaped core in the centre. This virus is interesting as being morphologically similar to some viruses which attack insects.

The intracellular localization of another large leafhopper-borne virus, that of potato yellow dwarf, has been studied by MacLeod *et al.* (1966). They find a striking association of the virus particles with the nuclei of infected cells. What appeared to be intranuclear virus inclusions were actually invaginations of the cytoplasm into the nucleus and these invaginations were surrounded by the nuclear envelope. In all the sections showing the association of virus particles with the nucleus, large numbers of virus particles were found to be present in expanded areas between the two lamellae of the nuclear envelope. It is suggested that this might be the site of virus replication, and it is also suggested that the inner lamella of the nuclear envelope might be incorporated into the membrane surrounding the virus particle.

Rice-dwarf virus particles found in *Oryza sativa* leaf cells are 400 to 600 Å in diameter, and occur in random distribution in masses or in crystalline array within the chlorotic tissue cells close to the vascular bundles (Fukushi *et al.*, 1960; Shikata, 1965). Wound-tumour virus particles within cells of *Melilotus alba* are 350 to 450 Å in diameter and appear usually in mass or random distribution in the tumour cells (Shikata *et al.*, 1964; Shikata, 1965). In both viruses the particles occur in the cytoplasm but not within the nucleus, mitochondria, or plastids.

As regards the visualization of isometric plant viruses in the insect vector, most of the successful results have been obtained with the large leafhopper-borne viruses, some of which can hardly be classified as isometric but are included here for convenience.

There is, however, one case of a small isometric plant virus being visualized inside the aphid vector. This is pea enation mosaic virus, and particles about 300 to 350 Å in diameter similar to those observed in the plant have been seen in the fatbody and gut lumen of viruliferous aphids (Plate 10) (Shikata and Maramorosch, 1965, 1966).

Probably the first electron micrographs showing the particles of a leaf-hopper-borne virus within the tissues of the insect vector were made by Fukushi *et al.* (1962), and by Fukushi and Shikata (1963). They showed clusters of virus particles of rice dwarf in the cells of the intestinal epithelium, Malpighian tubules, blood, ovaries, salivary glands, fatbody, and mycetomes. The virus occurred only in the cell cytoplasm and not in the nuclei or mitochondria. The particles were often in a crystalline array (Plate 11).

The wound-tumour virus has also been visualized inside the leaf-hopper vector *Agallia constricta* Van Duzee. Virus particles occur, often as microcrystals, in the cytoplasm of cells of fatbody, Malpighian tubules, intestines, mycetomes, muscles, tracheae, and epidermis (Shikata *et al.*, 1964; Shikata and Maramorosch, 1965).

Virus-like particles presumed to be the virus of maize mosaic have been seen in the vector *Peregrinus maidis* after it had acquired the virus by feeding on affected plants. The particles were seen in the salivary glands and epithelial cells of the intestinal wall. In the salivary glands the virus was found in the endoplasmic reticulum and in vacuole-like structures. In the intestinal cells the particles were seen in the peri-nuclear space and in tubules. The distribution of the virus suggests that development may take place in the endoplasmic reticulum (Herold and Munz, 1965).

From this brief survey of plant viruses *in situ* in plants and insects, it is clear that, so far as plants are concerned, some viruses occur in the cell nuclei, e.g. beet yellows virus (Cronshaw *et al.*, 1966), pea enation mosaic virus (Shikata *et al.*, 1966), and potato yellow dwarf virus (MacLeod *et al.*, 1966). Others such as lettuce necrotic yellows virus appeared to develop in the cytoplasm and were not found in the nucleus, mitochondria, or chloroplasts (Chambers *et al.*, 1965). A similar state of affairs occurs with rice dwarf virus and wound tumour virus (Shikata, 1965). There are one or two instances of viruses being found in the chloroplasts such as beet yellows virus (Cronshaw *et al.*, 1966). Leyon (1953) suggests that beet yellows virus is formed in the stroma of the chloroplasts, and Shalla (1964) observed particles of tobacco mosaic virus in the chloroplasts of cells of tomato leaf.

The virus of tomato spotted wilt is often associated with the endoplasmic reticulum, and Kitajima (1965) considers that the latter may be concerned in virus formation. Arnott and Smith (1967) point out an apparently close connexion between the endoplasmic reticulum and the intracellular inclusions in sunflower mosaic. It is not certain, however, that these inclusions consist of virus.

A similar association of virus with the endoplasmic reticulum occurs in the insect vector of maize mosaic, and this suggests that virus development may take place within this organelle (Herold and Munz, 1965).

There appear to be no published records of virus in the mitochondria of the higher plants. However, Lindegren and Bang (1964), studying a virus infection of yeasts, *Saccharomyces*, consider that the site of propagation of the virus is the mitochondrion.

# References

ARNOTT, H. J. and SMITH, K. M. (1967) *J. Ultrastruct. Res.* **19**, 173–95.
BAWDEN, F. C. (1964) *Plant Viruses and Virus Diseases*. 4th ed. New York: Ronald Press Co.
BILS, R. F. and HALL, C. E. (1962) *Virology*. **17**, 123.
BRANDES, J. and BERCKS, R. (1965) *Adv. Vir. Res.* **11**, 1–24.
BRANDES, J. and ZIMMER, K. (1955) *Phytopathol. Z.* **24**, 211.
CASPAR, D. L. D. (1964) in *Plant Virology*. pp. 267–91. Eds. M. K. Corbett, and H. D. Sisler. Gainesville: Univ. of Florida Press.
CHAMBERS, T. C., CROWLEY, N. C., and FRANCKI, R. I. B. (1965) *Virology*. **27**, 320–8.
CHAMBERS, T. C. and FRANCKI, R. I. B. (1966) *Virology*. **29**, 673–6.

E

CRICK, F. H. C. and WATSON, J. D. (1956) *Nature.* **177**, 473.

CRONSHAW, J., HOEFERT, L., and ESAU, K. (1966) *J. Cell Biol.* **31**, 429–43.

EDWARDSON, J. R. (1966a) *Amer. J. Botany.* **53**, 359.

EDWARDSON, J. R. (1966b) *Science.* **153**, 883.

FINCH, J. T. (1964) *J. Mol. Biol.* **8**, 872–4.

FINCH, J. T. and KLUG, A. (1966) *J. Mol. Biol.* **15**, 344–64.

FUKUSHI, T. and SHIKATA, E. (1963) *Virology.* **21**, 503.

FUKUSHI, T., SHIKATA, E., and KIMURA, I. (1960) *Proc. Japan Acad.* **36**, 352.

FUKUSHI, T., SHIKATA, E., and KIMURA, I. (1962) *Virology.* **18**, 192.

GIBBS, A. J., NIXON, H. L., and WOODS, R. D. (1963) *Virology.* **19**, 441–9.

HALL, C. E. (1958) *J. Amer. Chem. Soc.* **80**, 2556.

HARRISON, B. D. and CROWLEY, N. C. (1965) *Virology.* **26**, 297–310.

HARRISON, B. D. and WOODS, R. D. (1966) *Virology.* **28**, 610–20.

HART, R. G. (1955) *Proc. Natl. Acad. Sci. U.S.* **41**, 261.

HEROLD, F. and MUNZ, K. (1965) *Virology.* **25**, 412.

HEROLD, F., BERGOLD, G. H., and WEIBEL, J. (1960) *Virology.* **12**, 335.

HITCHBORN, J. H., HILLS, G. J., and HULL, R. (1966) *Virology.* **28**, 768–72.

HORNE, R. W., RUSSELL, G. E., and TRIM, A. R. (1959) *J. Mol. Biol.* **1**, 234.

HUXLEY, H. E. and ZUBAY, G. (1960) *J. Mol. Biol.* **2**, 189.

IE, T. S. (1964) *Neth. J. Plant Pathol.* **70**, 114.

KAESBERG, P. (1956) *Science.* **124**, 626–8.

KIKUMOTO, T. and MATSUI, C. (1962) *Virology.* **16**, 509–10.

KITAJIMA, E. W. (1965) *Virology.* **26**, 89.

KITAJIMA, E. W. and COSTA, A. S. (1966) *Virology.* **29**, 523–39.

KITAJIMA, E. W., SILVA, D. M., OLIVEIRA, A. R., MÜLLER, G. W., and COSTA, A. S. (1963) *Nature.* **201**, 1011.

KLUG, A. and CASPAR, D. L. D. (1960) *Adv. Vir. Res.* **7**, 225.

KLUG, A. and FINCH, J. T. (1960a) *J. Mol. Biol.* **2**, 201.

KLUG, A. and FINCH, J. T. (1960b) *J. Mol. Biol.* **2**, 434.

KLUG, A., LONGLEY, W., and LEBERMAN, R. (1966) *J. Mol. Biol.* **15**, 315–43.

LEYON, H. (1953) *Exp. Cell Res.* **4**, 362–70.

LINDEGREN, C. C. and BANG, Y. N. (1964) *Nature.* **203**, 431–2.

MACLEOD, R., BLACK, L. M., and MAYER, F. H. (1966) *Virology.* **29**, 540–52.

MARKHAM, R. (1951) *Discussions Faraday Soc.* **11**, 221.

MARKHAM, R., FREY, S., and HILLS, G. J. (1963) *Virology.* **20**, 88.

MARKHAM, R. and SMITH, K. M. (1949) *Parasitology.* **39**, 330–42.

MILNE, R. G. (1966) *Virology.* **28**, 79–89.

NIXON, H. L. and GIBBS, A. J. (1960) *J. Mol. Biol.* **2**, 197.

NIXON, H. L. and HARRISON, B. D. (1959) *J. Gen. Microbiol.* **21**, 582.

SHALLA, T. A. (1964) *J. Cell Biol.* **21**, 253.

SCHMIDT, H. B., RICHTER, J., HERTZSCH, W., and KLINKOWSKI, M. (1963) *Phytopathol. Z.* **47**, 66.

SCHRAMM, G., SCHUMACHER, G., and ZILLIG, W. (1955) *Nature.* **175**, 549.

SHIKATA, E. (1965) *Conf. Relationships Between Arthropods and Plant-Pathogenic Viruses.* 1965. Tokyo. (Jap. Soc. Prom. Sci.) p. 105.

SHIKATA, E. and MARAMOROSCH, K. (1965) *Conf. Relationships Between Arthropods and Plant-Pathogenic Viruses.* 1965. Tokyo. p. 160.

SHIKATA, E. and MARAMOROSCH, K. (1966) *Virology.* **30**, 439–54.

SHIKATA, E., MARAMOROSCH, K., and GRANADOS, R. R. (1966) *Virology.* **29**, 426–36.

SHIKATA, E., ORENSKI, S. W., HIRUMI, H., MITSUHASHI, J., and MARAMOROSCH, K. (1964) *Virology.* **23**, 441.

SMITH, K. M. (1956) *Virology.* **2**, 706.

STAHMAN, M. A. and KAESBERG, P. (1955) *Phytopathology.* **45**, 187–95.

STEERE, R. L. (1957) *J. biophys. biochem. cytol.* **3**, 45–60.

WILLIAMS, R. C. and SMITH, K. M. (1958) *Biochim. Biophys. Acta.* **28**, 464–9.

WILLIAMS, R. C. and STEERE, R. L. (1951) *J. Amer. Chem. Soc.* **73**, 2057.

# CHAPTER SIX

# Chemistry of Plant Viruses

Before any chemical analyses can be made of a plant virus, or indeed any virus, it is necessary to free it from the host cell materials, and we have already discussed some of the methods for doing this in Chapter Four. However, not all plant viruses are amenable to these purification techniques and out of the 300 or more plant viruses already described only about 10 per cent have been isolated in sufficient quantities for chemical analysis. As we have previously pointed out in Chapter Four, the essential conditions for purification are high concentration of virus in the host plant, not less than 2 mg per litre, stability of the virus under the necessary chemical treatments, suitability of the host plant, i.e. absence of tannins, mucilage, etc. in the plant sap, and possibly also a difference in size of the virus particles from that of the cell components.

Shortly after Stanley isolated the virus of tobacco mosaic in 1935, Bawden and Pirie (1936) showed that it was a nucleoprotein, and this is true of all viruses so far isolated and purified. In the small plant viruses there is no other constituent except protein and nucleic acid, and, if we except the bacterial viruses and the virus which attacks blue-green algae (Chapter Seven), the nucleic acid component is ribonucleic acid (RNA). Of the animal viruses and bacteriophages, some contain RNA and others contain deoxyribose nucleic acid (DNA), but no virus contains both types.

The two nucleic acids derive their names from the different sugars they contain, one D-ribofuranose and the other D-2-deoxyribofuranose, but they also differ in other respects. Both contain four nitrogenous compounds (bases) of which two are the *purines*, adenine and guanine, common to both types of nucleic acid, and two are *pyrimidines*, cytosine and uracil in RNA, and, usually, cytosine and thymine in DNA (Bawden, 1964).

It is fairly easy to separate the nucleic acid of TMV from its protein coat and this can be accomplished by the use of heat, alkali, sodium dodecylsulphate, glacial acetic acid, phenol, and detergents.

The important discovery that the nucleic acid of TMV was by itself infectious was made almost at the same time by Gierer and Schramm (1956) and by Fraenkel-Conrat (1956). This discovery was forecast by Markham and Smith (1949) who showed that the virus of turnip yellow mosaic (TYMV), when extracted from the plant, consisted of two morphologically similar types of particles, only one of which contained RNA. They further showed that only this particle was infectious, thus correlating infectivity with the presence of nucleic acid.

Infectious RNA has been isolated from turnip yellow mosaic virus degraded with 40 per cent ethanol at room temperature. In order to obtain preparations containing a high proportion of such RNA, it was necessary to use bentonite during the purification of the virus or to add bentonite before degrading the virus. These RNA preparations were shown to be infectious, both soon after preparation and after storage at $-22°C$ for 2 years. The infectivity was destroyed by incubation with ribonuclease and was equal to about 1 per cent of the infectivity of the intact virus. RNA could be extracted either from virus purified by differential centrifugation or by ammonium sulphate precipitation from sap clarified by either bentonite or ethanol (Dunn and Hitchborn, 1966).

This discovery of the infectivity of the nucleic acid indicates that herein lies the genetic material of the virus. Therefore, the RNA can not only reproduce itself but also controls the synthesis of its particular protein.

There is considerable evidence which shows that the RNA alone carries infectivity. Infectious suspensions of RNA are inactivated by the enzyme ribonuclease whereas whole virus is not. RNA is more easily destroyed by ultraviolet light and various chemicals and it is not affected by antiserum to the whole virus. In comparative inoculation tests with virus RNA and whole virus to *Nicotiana glutinosa*, the local lesions, characteristic of TMV infection in this plant, develop from 8 to 10 hours earlier with the RNA than with whole virus. The assumption here is that the delay in the appearance of the whole-virus lesions is due to the interval while the protein coat of the virus particle is discarded, this not being necessary with naked RNA. In high-speed centrifugation of whole TMV and RNA, the former is sedimented but the latter is not, the supernatant being still infective. Furthermore, no virus particles can be detected by means of electron microscopy.

Viruses reconstituted from the protein of one strain and the RNA of another always show the characteristics of the strain supplying the RNA.

Bawden (1964) has pointed out that, with the advent of chromatography, knowledge of the composition of viruses has increased rapidly. It is now possible not only to have quantitative analysis for the amino acids composing the proteins and the nucleotides of the nucleic acid, but also to have the sequence of the amino acids in the proteins determined.

The main component of plant viruses is the protein and varies from about 95 per cent in TMV to about 65 per cent in turnip yellow mosaic virus (TYMV). The difference between strains of the same virus lies mainly in their proteins and the following account of protein differences in virus strains is quoted from Knight (1964).

(1) The proteins of strains often differ from one another in proportions of some of their constituent amino acids, the rest of the amino acids appearing to be present in the same proportions.

(2) In some strains, certain amino acids are present which are completely lacking in others (notably histidine and methionine).

(3) Strains which have arisen from a common strain presumably by few mutational steps are very similar in protein composition and, at the extreme, may in fact be identical.

(4) Differences in strain proteins, when they occur, may involve almost any of the constituent amino acids.

(5) The observation that strains arising from few mutational steps have correspondingly few amino acid changes suggests that in some cases, at least, mutation involves stepwise changes in amino acid content.

The results of a study of the amino acid and nucleotide composition of two biologically distinct strains of southern bean mosaic virus, from bean and cowpea respectively, may appropriately be quoted here. The nucleotide composition of the two virus strains was similar. Amino acid analyses indicated that both virus proteins were composed of approximately 270 amino acid residues and both had a subunit molecular weight of 29,000. There were differences between the two virus proteins in at least 21 amino acids (Tremaine, 1966).

The following are the chemical constituents of strain Y of cucumber mosaic virus: 1·8 per cent phosphorus and 16·4 per cent nitrogen. Its base ratio is: adenine, 24·3; guanine, 23·4; cytosine, 23·2; and uracil, 29·0 per cent. It has an RNA content of 18·5 per cent (Kaper et al., 1965).

The tobacco mosaic virus particle consists of protein and RNA in the proportion of 94·5:5·6. The general elementary composition of the common or field type of virus is: carbon, 50; hydrogen, 7; nitrogen, 16·6; sulphur, 0·2; phosphorus, 0·53; ash, 1·5; and carbohydrate 2·5 per cent. The nucleic acid exists as a single polynucleotide chain of some 6,400 residues, and it has a molecular weight of $2 \times 10^6$. The protein consists of 2,130 identical molecules or subunits, each of which has a molecular weight of 17,500 and consists of 158 amino acids (Siegel, 1965).

The RNA of wound tumour virus (WTV) which attacks clover has been recently shown to be double-stranded (Black and Markham, 1963). It is interesting that the only other double-stranded RNA occurs in a group of animal viruses, the reoviruses to which WTV has a morphological resemblance. Indeed, a serological relationship between the two has been suggested (Streissle and Maramorosch, 1963 a and b).

## References

BAWDEN, F. C. (1964) *Plant Viruses and Virus Diseases*. 4th ed. New York: Ronald Press Co.

BAWDEN, F. C. and PIRIE, N. W. (1936) *Brit. J. exp. Path.* **17**, 64.

BLACK, L. and MARKHAM, R. (1963) *Neth. J. Plant Pathol.* **69**, 215.

DUNN, D. B. and HITCHBORN, J. H. (1966) *Virology.* **30**, 598–607.

FRAENKEL-CONRAT, H. (1956) *J. Amer. Chem. Soc.* **78**, 882.

GIERER, A. and SCHRAMM, G. (1956) *Nature.* **177**, 702.

KAPER, J. M., DIENER, T. O., and SCOTT, H. A. (1965) *Virology.* **27**, 54–72.

KNIGHT, C. A. (1964) in *Plant Virology.* pp. 292–314. Eds. M. K. Corbett, and H. D. Sisler. Gainesville: Univ. of Florida Press.

MARKHAM, R. and SMITH, K. M. (1949) *Parasitology.* **39**, 330–42.

SIEGEL, A. (1965) *Adv. Vir. Res.* **11**, 25–60.

STANLEY, W. M. (1935) *Science N. S.* **81**, 644–5.

STREISSLE, G. and MARAMOROSCH, K. (1963a) *Science.* **140**, 996.

STREISSLE, G. and MARAMOROSCH, K. (1963b) *Phytopathology.* **53**, 891.

TREMAINE, J. H. (1966) *Virology.* **30**, 348–54.

# CHAPTER SEVEN

# Infection and Replication. Incomplete Viruses. Satellite Viruses

## Infection and Replication

It is now generally accepted that the first event to occur when a virus particle enters a susceptible cell is the release of the nucleic acid or, in other words, the protein coat is stripped off the particle. This probably takes place by a stepwise removal of the protein subunits since this is what happens in the degradation of TMV in alkaline solutions.

It must be remembered that in the synthesis of viruses two kinds of fundamentally different processes are involved: (a) 'reading' the viral genetic information and carrying into effect the messages which it contains; and (b) 'copying' this information in order to reproduce identically the nucleic acid moiety of the infecting particle. These processes can be accomplished only if the coat protein is removed from the nucleic acid (Mundry, 1963).

Numerous studies have been carried out to investigate the site of virus multiplication in the cell and its movement therefrom. Most of this work has been performed with TMV, and the sequence seems to be from nucleolus to cytoplasm.

Although electron microscopy seldom reveals TMV in the nucleus, there is a good deal of evidence that the nucleus plays a part in virus synthesis. Various techniques have been employed to study this process and they include ultraviolet light, phase, and electron microscopy and a labelling technique with uridine-$H^3$ and cytidine-$H^3$.

In addition, the technique of fluorescent antibody staining has been used by Hirai and Hirai (1964). They showed that, soon after injection of TMV, a temporary fluorescence was observed near the site of virus injection. This soon disappeared and about 6 hours after injection a new fluorescent antibody reaction could be detected. This was mainly confined to the nucleus and to the adjoining cytoplasm. Hirai and coworkers (Takahashi and Hirai, 1963; Hirai and Wildman, 1963; Hirai and Nakagaki, 1966) have demonstrated large amounts of RNA in infected nuclei and RNA accumulation in cytoplasmic inclusions, and have given proof of the appearance of virus protein in the nucleus.

From all these experiments there is, as pointed out by Bald (1966), convincing evidence for the common form of TMV in tobacco that both virus protein and RNA are formed in the nucleus.

Leaf hairs which consist of a single chain of cells provide a good system for cytological studies of virus multiplication. Hair cells were inoculated near the tip with TMV by decapitation and insertion of a thin gelatin-virus solution; this was followed by capping with a thicker gel. Cell-to-cell passage of the virus RNA gave an indication of the natural infection process. While the infection was spreading down the chain of hair cells, however, substrate for virus multiplication was being drawn up from the base. The most recently infected cells were in a position to intercept substrate needed by the more distal cells, still actively synthesizing virus. Competition for substrate apparently had little effect on the initiation of infection and virus multiplication (Zech, 1952; Hirai and Hirai, 1964).

Bald (1964 a and b) has made observations on the reaction of tobacco cells to common TMV during the phase of virus multiplication when cytoplasmic flow increased and before floccules containing RNA and virus monolayers began to appear in the cell. In infected cells during the period of cytoplasmic activity, there were cycles in the nucleolus and nucleus that were connected with the production of RNA. Material that in fixed preparations stained like RNA and was ribonuclease-sensitive was given off by the nucleolus and passed through the nucleus to the cytoplasm. This was observed under phase-contrast microscopy and recorded in fixed and stained preparations.

Wettstein and Zech (1962), using the electron microscope, have also observed passage of material, thought to be RNA, of the common strain of TMV from the nucleus into the cytoplasm. The nucleus became so deeply grooved that it was 'traversed by an elaborate system of cytoplasmic channels'. Bits of nuclear material about the size of small cell organelles were pinched off surrounded by portions of the nuclear envelope, and apparently found their way out through the cytoplasmic channels. This may be similar to the extrusion of RNA described by Bald (1964 a and b).

In electron microscope studies of potato yellow dwarf virus in the cell, MacLeod *et al.* (1966) described somewhat similar happenings. In this case there appear to be invaginations of cytoplasmic inclusions containing virus into the nucleus and these invaginations were surrounded by the nuclear envelope (see Chapter Five).

Smith and Schlegel (1965) carried out experiments with radio-active tracers using the common form of TMV in tobacco. They found that the nucleolus was the centre of RNA synthesis, 2 days after inoculation. DNA-directed synthesis of RNA was inhibited with Actinomycin D. In inhibited infected tissues after 4 hours of uridine-H³ feeding, label appeared in the nucleus and most heavily in the nucleolus.

Electron microscope studies have been made of an unidentified virus affecting the wild plant *Lantana horrida*. Micrographs show quantities of virus apparently in process of assembly in both cytoplasm and nucleus. The virus, which is a very long rod, occurs in regular arrays in both situations, together with helices equal in length to the virus rods and crystalline material from which the helices appear to be assembled (Arnott and Smith, unpublished).

The cytology and replication of tomato spotted wilt virus (TSWV), which differs greatly in its properties from TMV, have been studied by Bald and Solberg (1962). They used a strain of the virus which occurred in high concentration in the host and which produced little necrosis. The sequence of events seemed very similar to that of TMV; these events included turbulence in the cytoplasm near the nucleus, nucleolar cycles, association of the nucleus with plastids, and the appearance of included ribonuclease-sensitive material in the cytoplasm. Later, X-bodies formed from material in the cytoplasm. Virus synthesis seemed to be initiated in the nucleolus, but RNA and virus protein were probably assembled in the cytoplasm in association with the endoplasmic reticulum.

The specific turbulent areas in the cytoplasm, termed 'cytoplasmic vortices' by Bald, in which virus assembly appears to take place, might be compared to similar cytoplasmic areas in virus-infected caterpillars

(Smith, 1967). These have been called 'virogenic stroma' and are centres of virus assembly.

Before concluding this short account of the infection and replication processes of plant viruses, it may be of interest to refer briefly to similar processes in a virus affecting the blue-green alga *Plectonema boryanum*. This is a very small filamentous organism with photosynthetic lamellae and a nuclear area, or nucleoplasm, in the place of chloroplasts and nucleus. It is considered to be more nearly related to the bacteria than some of the other algae.

The infection of *P. boryanum* by a virus was first recorded by Safferman and Morris (1963) and they suggested that the virus particle is an icosahedron with a short tail. Subsequently, the virus was shown to contain DNA (Schneider *et al.*, 1964).

In two publications (Smith *et al.*, 1966 a and b), the methods of culturing the alga and its virus and some aspects of the infection process were described. It was demonstrated that actually the virus has a long tail by which it is attached to the cell wall of the filament. It is thought that the cell is infected by this means and that the DNA is injected through the tail after the manner of some bacteriophages. The length of the 'tail' is disputed by some workers.

The development of the virus in the algal cell has been followed by electron microscopy of thin sections and it exhibits some interesting and unusual features. A section through an algal cell 16 hours after infection shows large numbers of the fully formed near-spherical virus particles (Plate 12)

A similar section through a cell 1 hour or less after infection shows, instead of the virus, numbers of particles with an elongated profile (Plate 13). At higher magnification these are shown to be helices (Plate 13 inset), the diameter of the coil being approximately 180 Å and of the threads composing the coil about 20 Å. The number of loops in the helix has not been definitely ascertained but there seem to be at least three. At a very early stage of infection, numerous small particles are visible between the photosynthetic lamellae of the cell. Some of these are probably the so-called 'alpha particles' normally present in the cell, but others are larger and appear to be helices in process of formation. The tentative suggestion is made that the following sequence of events forms the replication cycle of the virus. After injection of the DNA into the cell, formation of the viral DNA takes place in the nucleoplasm, whence it migrates to the photosynthetic lamellae where the helices can be seen in process of formation. The next event seems to be the movement of the helices into the virogenic stroma. These further changes takę place, the helix becomes enclosed in its protein coat and condenses into the near-spherical shape of the mature particle. In sections of particles at this stage of formation, the loops of the helix are still visible (Brown *et al.*, 1966; Smith *et al.*, 1967). The exact nature of this rather large helix is still uncertain. It is thought to be composite and to be made up of DNA helices which are themselves twisted into a helical formation.

For a detailed account of the infection and replication processes of plant viruses the reader is referred to a comprehensive review by Bald (1966).

### Incomplete Viruses

Several cases are known in which the replication mechanism of viruses seems to go astray with the consequent formation of incomplete or imperfect virus particles, but the underlying causes of these abnormalities are not known. One of the first examples of this kind of anomaly is given by the 'top' and 'bottom' components of the turnip yellow mosaic virus (TYMV), in which morphologically similar particles are formed, but only one, the bottom component, contains RNA and is infectious (Markham and Smith, 1949). What may be a similar breakdown in the linear replication mechanism occurs in the granulosis, an insect virus, in which the apparently unlimited production of long threads occurs. (Smith and Brown, 1965).

The most detailed study of incomplete plant viruses has been made by Siegel *et al.* (1962) on tobacco mosaic virus and much of this information is derived from their work. It was observed that no infectivity could be recovered from a large proportion of lesions induced by TMV treated with nitrous acid which produces mutants (Siegel, 1965). The suggestion was made that these sterile lesions arise from infections by virus particles which were defective in their ability to synthesize the protein coat. Several defective mutants were isolated, following nitrous acid treatment of TMV by limit dilution (Siegel *et al.*, 1962), a procedure which does not involve the transfer of infectivity from local lesions.

The mutants which were isolated all had several features in common: (a) no infectious whole-virus particles could be detected in homogenates of infected leaves; (b) almost no infectivity could be recovered from necrotic local lesions; (c) the infectious agent is unstable in leaf homogenates; and (d) the symptom patterns induced in a systemic host are all similar, suggesting a slow cell-to-cell movement without transport in the conducting elements as happens with infections with normal TMV. Three types of defective mutants of TMV were isolated and designated as $PM_2$, $PM_1$, and $PM_4$.

(1) Plants infected with $PM_2$ contain a virus-like protein which can aggregate reversibly. It is defective in the sense that it will not reconstitute with TMV nucleic acid to form intact infectious rods. The $PM_2$ protein will aggregate linearly, but it forms rods which differ in their structure from that of a normal TMV rod. Instead of the tight helix or stacked-disc configuration of the normal rod, the $PM_2$ protein aggregates into a loose double helix, the strands of which become very long on standing. In addition, the $PM_2$ protein differs from that of the parent strain of TMV by 2 amino acid replacements in the 158 amino acid sequence.

(2) The second type of defective strain, $PM_1$, does not induce the formation of a virus-like protein which can aggregate into rods. At first it was thought that no protein at all was synthesized, because the infective plant juice did not form a precipitate with TMV antiserum (see Chapter Eleven). However, by the use of serological methods, it was concluded that the $PM_1$ protein is present in a disaggregated form, because it reacts best with antibodies to disaggregated virus protein.

(3) In the third type of mutant, $PM_4$, infected leaf homogenates contain small quantities of a non-infectious rod-like material which behaves like TMV in the preparative ultracentrifuge. In addition the material contains a protein which aggregates reversibly.

It is interesting to note that the movement or translocation of these defective viruses is apparently restricted to a cell-to-cell movement presumably through the plasmodesmata. There seems to be no movement by way of the conducting elements, possibly because the naked RNA would be subject to enzyme action. Thus, systemic infection is probably brought about by movement of whole virus and this is supported by the work of Esau *et al.* (1967), where quantities of sugar-beet yellows virus, a long flexuous rod, can be seen apparently in process of passing through the plasmodesmata.

The fact that virus infections can exist without the presence of visible virus particles may have an important bearing relative to some of the animal tumours which are suspected to be of viral origin but in which no virus particles can be demonstrated.

This discussion of defective viruses leads naturally to the contemplation of another form of incomplete viruses known as the satellite viruses.

## Satellite Viruses

Sometimes one virus may depend upon the assistance of another virus in the same cell to help it perform a necessary function of its existence. One form of such assistance is described in Chapter Eight, where the virus of tobacco mottle is shown to be dependent upon the presence of the vein-distorting virus in the same plant for its transmission by the aphid vector.

The form of dependence with which we are concerned here is even more fundamental because it deals with the vital function of replication. In other words, here is a situation in which one virus lacks the power of multiplication without the presence of a second virus to supply the necessary aid. Such a situation is known as 'satellitism' and the incomplete virus as a 'satellite virus'. In the case both of the mottle virus and of the satellite, the helping virus is specific; just any other virus will not do.

In his review of satellitism and related phenomena, Kassanis (1967) has introduced some terms which need explanation. He uses the term 'satellite' for any virus that is invariably associated with, and seems entirely dependent on, another virus. The term 'activator' is applied to the virus that allows the satellite virus to infect and multiply and the phenomenon is called 'activation'. Kassanis (1962) was the first to describe the satellite virus (SV), which has been found only in association with tobacco necrosis virus (TNV), the latter being the activator. TNV is often found alone and multiplies indefinitely in plants without the production of SV, which has to be introduced as such. SV is a very small virus measuring only 17 m$\mu$ in diameter; it has an RNA content of 20 per cent by weight and its maximum molecular weight is 340,000.

Both viruses occur in the roots of apparently normal plants and both are transmitted between roots by the spores of the fungus *Olpidium brassicae* (see Chapter Eight). Three facts to bear in mind about SV are: (*a*) SV cannot multiply by itself; (*b*) TNV alone can multiply indefinitely without causing the production of SV; (*c*) the two viruses are antigenically unrelated and their antigenicity is not influenced by the activator, but depends on the strain of SV used in the inoculation, showing that the protein of SV is coded by its RNA (Kassanis, 1965). Since SV codes for its own protein shell, it is not for synthesis of its protein that help is required, but what SV actually obtains from the activator is not at present known. SV appears to be the only complete and stable virus particle known which requires another virus to help in its synthesis.

Another example of satellitism is given by the tobacco rattle virus which is also soil-transmitted, but by root-feeding nematodes and not by fungal spores (see Chapter Eight). This virus is unusual in that rods of different lengths occur in infected plants, one about 80 m$\mu$ and the other about 185 m$\mu$, both having the same diameter of 25 m$\mu$ (Harrison and Nixon, 1959). Tobacco rattle virus often occurs in unstable form, i.e. as nucleic acid which is inactivated by the action of leaf ribonuclease. Phenol extracts from leaves containing the unstable form are much more infective than water extracts, the phenol extracting more RNA than water does. (Sänger and Brandenberg, 1961; Cadman, 1962.)

The two types of rattle virus were first described by Want and Rozendaal (1948) but their significance was not understood till some years later. Lister (1966) found that whether inocula produced stable or unstable virus depended upon the presence of the short particles in the inoculum.

His results suggest that the long particles fail to produce stable virus because their nucleic acid is deficient in the information required either for the synthesis of the virus protein or for the assembly of the virus nucleic acid and protein into complete virus particles. It is thought that this deficiency is made good by the RNA of the short particles, which, though unable to infect and multiply on their own, code for the protein of both long and short particles.

Lister's results were confirmed by Frost *et al.* (1967) who used a Brazilian strain of tobacco rattle virus which had an unusually short particle, making it easier to separate from the long particles by gradient centrifugation. They found that increasing quantities of short particles, in inocula containing a constant amount of long particles, produced an increasing proportion of lesions containing stable virus. Frost *et al.* agreed with Lister in finding that short particles were effective in aiding protein synthesis only when inoculated together with long particles of the same strain.

Kassanis (1967) points out that the association between the two particles of strains of tobacco rattle virus can perhaps be described as symbiosis because both particles contribute and benefit more or less equally. The short particles alone are not infective and need to be activated by the long particles; in return the short particles provide the protein for both. The short particle is in effect a satellite of the long particle and, like the satellite virus of tobacco necrosis virus, is completely dependent for its existence on the activator.

A difference between SV and tobacco rattle virus, however, should be noted. Whereas SV and its activator, tobacco necrosis virus, are serologically unrelated, the two interacting particles of the tobacco rattle virus association are considered to be two particles of the same virus.

## References

BALD, J. G. (1964a) *Virology*. **22**, 377–87.

BALD, J. G. (1964b) *Virology*. **22**, 388–96.

BALD, J. G. (1966) in *Adv. Vir. Res.* **12**, 103–25.

BALD, J. G. and SOLBERG, R. A. (1962) *Phytopathology*. **52**, 723–4 (Abstr.)

BROWN, R. M., SMITH, K. M., AND WALNE, P. L. (1966) *Nature*. **212**, 729–30.

CADMAN, C. H. (1962) *Nature*. **193**, 49.

ESAU, K., CRONSHAW, J., and HOEFERT, L. L. (1966) *Proc. Natl. Acad. Sci. U.S.* **55**, 486–93.

FROST, R. R., HARRISON, B. D., and WOODS, R. D. (1967) *J. gen. Virology* (in press).

HARRISON, B. D. and NIXON, H. L. (1959) *J. Gen. Microbiol.* **21**, 569.

HIRAI, T. and HIRAI, A. (1964) *Science*. **145**, 589–91.

HIRAI, T. and NAKAGAKI, Y. (1966) in *Viruses of Plants*. Eds. A. B. R. Beemster and J. Dijkstra. pp. 90–3. Amsterdam: North-Holland Publ. Co.

HIRAI, T. and WILDMAN, S. G. (1963) *Plant Cell Physiol.* (*Tokyo*) **4**, 265–75.

KASSANIS, B. (1962) *J. Gen. Microbiol.* **27**, 477–88.

KASSANIS, B. (1965) *Ann. Inst. Phytopath. Benaki.* **6**, 7–26.

KASSANIS, B. (1967) *Adv. Vir. Res.* **13** (in press).

LISTER, R. M. (1966) *Virology.* **28, 350.**

MACLEOD, R., BLACK, L. M., and MAYER, F. H. (1966) *Virology.* **29,** 540–52.

MARKHAM, R. and SMITH, K. M. (1949) *Parasitology.* **39,** 330–42.

MUNDRY, K. W. (1963) *Ann. Rev. Phytopathol.* **1,** 173–96.

SAFFERMAN, R. S. and MORRIS, M. E. (1963) *Science.* **140,** 679–80.

SÄNGER, H. L. and BRANDENBERG, E. (1961) *Naturwissenschaften.* **48,** 391.

SCHNEIDER, I. R., DIENER, T. O., and SAFFERMAN, R. S. (1964) *Science.* **144,** 1127–30.

SIEGEL, A. (1965) *Adv. Vir. Res.* **11,** 40.

SIEGEL, A., ZAITLIN, M., and SEHGAL, O. P. (1962) *Proc. Natl. Acad. Sci. U.S.* **48,** 1845.

SMITH, K. M. (1967) *Insect Virology.* New York: Academic Press.

SMITH, K. M. and BROWN, R. M. (1965) *Virology.* **27,** 512–19.

SMITH, K. M., BROWN, R. M., GOLDSTEIN, D. A., and WALNE, P. L. (1966a) *Virology.* **28,** 580–91.

SMITH, K. M., BROWN, R. M., WALNE, P. L., and GOLDSTEIN, D. A. (1966b) *Virology.* **30,** 182–92.

SMITH, K. M., BROWN, R. M., and WALNE, P. L. (1967) *Virology.* **31,** 329–37.

SMITH, S. H. and SCHLEGEL, D. E. (1965) *Virology.* **26,** 180–9.

TAKAHASHI, T. and HIRAI, T. (1963) *Virology.* **19,** 431–40.

WANT, J. P. H. VAN DER and ROZENDAAL, A. (1948) *Tijdschr. PlZiekt.* **54,** 134.

WETTSTEIN, D. VON and ZECH, H. (1962) *Z. Naturforsch.* **17b,** 376–9.

ZECH, H. (1952) *Planta.* **40,** 461–514.

F

# CHAPTER EIGHT

# Transmission by Vectors

Plant viruses are more dependent on an organism for their transfer from infected to healthy plants than any other kind of pathogen. In the early days of plant virus research, it was considered that the power to transmit viruses was the property of only a few insects whose feeding methods specifically fitted them to achieve this. At the present time, however, one is compelled to change this view. It has been demonstrated that almost all types of organism feeding upon, or parasitizing, plants are capable of acting as vectors and these include biting and sucking insects, mites, nematode worms, and Chytrid fungi. Furthermore, every gradation of relationship between vector and virus exists, from a purely mechanical contamination of the jaws to an intimate biological association.

Before discussing the various aspects of vector-transmission, mention should be made of the inability of vectors to transmit the most infectious plant virus known, that of tobacco mosaic. The whole question has been investigated by Orlob (1963) but some recent work by Pirone (1967) is relevant here. Aphids (*Myzus persicae* Sulz.) were allowed to feed on a purified solution of TMV through a parafilm membrane and then allowed to probe a buffer solution, which was later tested and found to be infective. These results showed that infectious TMV can be acquired and released by aphids; the reason for the lack of transmission to plants must therefore lie in the inoculation process.

Among the possible reasons for lack of transmission suggested by Pirone are: (*a*) areas of the plant probed by aphids are not susceptible to TMV; (*b*) the TMV carried by the aphid although released into buffer solutions is not released at the plant sites probed; (*c*) the amount of TMV carried by the aphid is not sufficient to cause infection at the sites probed by the aphid although it is sufficient to cause infection when mechanically inoculated.

It is proposed to take the various types of vector in turn and to discuss their association with the viruses they transmit.

## Insecta

*Coleoptera, beetles. Orthoptera, grasshoppers, earwigs*

As might be expected, the type of association between viruses and insects with biting mouthparts, such as the above, is mainly of a purely mechanical nature. This has been demonstrated by Walters (1952) who showed that the large grasshopper, *Melanoplus existientialis*, would carry the virus of tobacco mosaic on its jaws and infect a healthy tobacco plant after first feeding on a mosaic-infected plant. However, the statement that all biting insects which transmit plant viruses do so in a purely mechanical manner should be modified slightly so far as the transmission of turnip yellow mosaic virus (TYMV) is concerned. In this case the transmitting agent must not only be a biting insect it must lack salivary glands. In the discussion on the transmission of plant viruses by aphids and other hemipterous insects, it will be shown that the saliva plays an important part in that process. It is interesting therefore to find that the absence of saliva in biting insects is the essential fact in the transmission of TYMV. Although the turnip flea beetle, *Phyllotreta* spp., is the natural vector of this virus in the field, it can be transmitted by any type of beetle that will feed on the appropriate plants. The explanation seems to be as follows. Since beetles have no salivary glands, it is necessary for them to regurgitate part of the contents of the foregut while eating; this is apparently necessary to help the digestion process. Regurgitation brings into contact with the leaf any infective tissue previously eaten and this, during mastication, is inoculated to a healthy susceptible plant. Transmission of this type is not confined to beetles so far as TYMV is concerned, and it can be spread by grasshoppers and earwigs (Forficulidae) which feed in a similar manner. The virus, however, is not spread by caterpillars, which are also biting insects, but they possess salivary glands and do not regurgitate while feeding. Transmitting beetles, or their larvae, can retain infective power for several days without further access to a source of virus; this is thought to be due merely to the length of time infective tissue remains in the foregut. When this is digested, the insect must feed once more on an infected plant before it can again transmit the virus (Markham and Smith, 1949). Although this type of transmission is slightly more complex than the purely mechanical method, there is no true biological relationship between virus and vector.

Further cases of beetle-transmitted viruses have been recently recorded. The virus of cocksfoot mottle (CFMV) is transmitted by the cereal leaf beetle (*Lema melanopa* L.). The beetles retained infectivity for as long as two weeks after feeding (Serjeant, 1967a). The virus of radish mosaic, *Raphanus sativus* L., is inefficiently transmitted by the beetles *Phyllotreta* spp. and *Diabrotica undecimpunctata* (Campbell and Colt, 1967).

## Hemiptera

All members of the Hemiptera feed in the same way, by means of sucking mouthparts which consist of two pairs of stylets, mandibles and maxillae, sliding in the grooved labium. Grooves on the inner faces of the stylets meet together to form two canals, down one of which saliva is injected into the plant while a mixture of sap and saliva passes up the other. Thus, such insects are ideally equipped for virus transmission.

## Aphididae

The great majority of plant viruses are transmitted by aphids and one species alone, *Myzus persicae*, is the vector of 50 different viruses.

The relationship between viruses and aphids is in no way a straightforward one and, in spite of a great deal of investigation and many ingenious theories, there is still much which is obscure.

Kennedy *et al.* (1962) have introduced terms which are descriptive of the relationship between insect and virus and which give some indication of the location of, and route followed by, the virus in the insect. The term 'stylet-borne' indicates that type of virus which adheres to the stylets after penetration of a virus-infected plant and is thus possibly in the category of mechanical transmission, though it is probably not as simple as that. A stylet-borne virus can be picked up by the insect almost immediately after feeding and transmitted to a susceptible healthy plant; all this can be accomplished in a minute or so. In serial transfers in this kind of transmission, usually only the first plant is in-fected and the insect then loses its infectivity. 'Circulative' viruses are swallowed by the aphid and have to pass through the gut wall into the blood and so back to the salivary glands before the insect becomes in-fective. In serial transfers with this type of virus, the first two or three plants remain healthy and infection usually appears in the third or fourth plant, depending on the time interval between transfers. This delay is presumably the time taken for the virus to pass through the gut of the insect and reach the salivary glands before it can be ejected into the plant.

'Propagative' viruses are those which have a definite biological rela-tionship with their vector; these viruses have been shown to multiply within the insect and are mainly leaf hopper-transmitted.

*Stylet-borne Viruses.* The following facts about the stylet-borne viruses have been elucidated by Watson and her co-workers (Watson, 1936; Watson and Roberts, 1939).

(1) A preliminary fasting period by the aphid greatly increases its capacity to transmit virus.

(2) A short feed (acquisition feed) is more effective than a long period of feeding, and aphids making many penetrations retained infectivity longer than those making prolonged single penetrations.

(3) Prolonged feeding reduces the efficiency of virus transmission.

It must also be remembered that there is another phenomenon in relation to stylet-borne viruses which is at present unexplained, i.e. the question of aphid specificity. In other words, one species of aphid can transmit a particular virus while another apparently similar species is unable to do so.

Some rather complicated, but not very precise, theories have been put forward to account for this phenomenon (Watson and Roberts, 1939; Day and Irzykiewicz, 1954; Van der Want, 1954; and Sylvester, 1954).

The idea of a purely mechanical process was reintroduced by Bradley (1952), and later (1959) he emphasized the role of aphid be-haviour in at least some of these transmission phenomena.

It was noticed that after a fasting period the aphid tended to make a number of very short penetrations of the leaf, mainly in the epidermis where many of the stylet-borne viruses are located. Furthermore, saliva was not secreted and virus contamination occurred during these short penetrations.

Bradley also observed that many aphids, when removed from a feeding position, have the stylets protruding beyond the tip of the rostrum. It is not possible for these thin and delicate stylets to pierce the leaf epidermis unsupported; the aphid must therefore wait until the rostrum is again extended down over them.

The behaviour of the aphid then offers two reasons why a preliminary starving period enhances virus transmission. First, it allows time for the extended stylets to be restored to their proper position for leaf penetration; second, it encourages numerous short stabs into the epidermis which appear to offer optimum conditions for transmission of the virus.

Another of the observations made by Watson was that the longer the aphid fed on the diseased plant the less efficient it became as a vector. This may be partly explained by the fact that the stylets penetrate, during prolonged feeding, into deeper tissues where the stylet-borne viruses are not located. If sections are cut through the spot in a leaf where an aphid has been feeding, it is possible by special staining to pick out the exact route followed by the insect's stylets (Smith, 1965). This is known as the 'stylet track', and it consists mainly of the aphid's saliva which has been moulded into a gelatinous tube by the movements of the stylets. Sylvester (1962) noticed that during brief penetrations of 15 to 20 seconds the salivary sheath was incomplete, and examination of the stylets, after such brief penetration, revealed a plug of saliva clinging to the tips of the stylets which is brought into contact with the tip of the labium when the latter ensheaths the stylets. Thus, virus-contaminated material will be smeared over the tip of the rostrum and the stylets, thereby being inoculated into the cell at the next penetration. On the other hand, prolonged feeding tends to eliminate transmission, as the stylets would have to be withdrawn through the long close-fitting salivary tube and this would tend to remove any virus-contaminated material adhering to them.

In brief, the transmission of the stylet-borne viruses can be partially explained by mechanical adherence of the virus to about $15\mu$ of the distal end of the stylets. Most of the other phenomena associated with this type of virus transmission are explainable in terms of aphid behaviour.

The problem of aphid specifity for different viruses, however, is still not satisfactorily solved.

The number of viruses which falls into the stylet-borne category is very large and cannot be enumerated here. It must suffice to give one group: this is the so-called 'Potato Virus Y' group. They are all long, flexuous, thread-like particles and include, in addition to potato virus Y, beet mosaic, tobacco etch, henbane (*Hyoscyamus*) mosaic, and bean yellow mosaic viruses. Incidentally, all these viruses produce the peculiar 'pinwheel' type of intracellular inclusions described in Chapter Two.

*Circulative Viruses.* Although one cannot specify the exact relationship which exists between this type of virus and the aphid, it is obviously more intimate than is the case with the stylet-borne viruses. This is made clear by the fact that there is a delay in the development of infective power, probably due to the time taken for the virus to pass through the gut into the blood and so back to the salivary glands. Many of the circulative viruses are not mechanically transmissible, and this may be because they are mainly located in the phloem rather than in the more superficial cell layers in which the stylet-borne viruses are found. In the case of the circulative virus of pea enation mosaic (PEMV), some work by Nault *et al.* (1964) shows that it is retained by the aphid vector after moulting, 11 out of 16 aphids transmitting virus after 3 moults. Any virus transmitted by an aphid after a moult must have been retained in the mid-gut, since the linings of fore- and hind-gut are shed. There is evidently a biological relationship of some kind between PEMV and the aphid vector, and it was the first virus to be visualized inside the aphid vector by electron microscopy (see Plate 10). Other differences between stylet-borne and circulative viruses are the longer periods of retention by aphids of the circulative viruses, and the facts that preliminary starving does not influence subsequent transmission, while prolonged initial feeding increases rather than decreases the likelihood of virus transmission.

Examples of circulative viruses are those of potato leaf-roll (Smith, 1931; Day, 1955), pea enation mosaic (Osborn, 1935; Chaudhuri, 1950;

Simons, 1954), barley yellow dwarf (Toko and Bruehl, 1959), and radish yellows (Duffus, 1960). The two components causing the rosette disease of tobacco, the vein-distorting and mottle viruses, are also both circulative; the aphid vector *Myzus persicae* retains these for a period of 30 days and probably for the remainder of its life (Smith, 1946).

*Propagative Viruses.* In the discussion on the relationship of plant viruses with leafhopper vectors convincing evidence that certain viruses do multiply in these insects will be presented. The situation as regards propagative viruses in aphids is less clear-cut, but there are one or two instances where the evidence for virus multiplication in the aphid is fairly convincing.

One of these concerns the virus of potato leaf-roll and the aphid vector *Myzus persicae*. It was with this virus that the serial inoculation technique, used for some years with leafhoppers, was first applied to aphids.

It was shown by Smith (1931) that the aphid *Myzus persicae* retained infectivity with the leaf-roll virus, even after feeding on an immune plant, such as cabbage, for as long as 7 days. In 1955, Day also presented evidence which suggested the possibility that the potato leaf-roll virus might multiply in the aphid *Myzus persicae*. In the same year, Heinze (1955) carried out experiments on the inoculation of aphids with plant extracts which opened the way to the subsequent work carried out by Stegwee and Ponsen (1958). Aphids were injected with aphid haemolymph and not with plant extracts which tend to be toxic to the insect. It was found that, after injection with haemolymph from virus-bearing (viruliferous) aphids, about 50 per cent of the injected aphids became infective after an average incubation period of 20 hours. When the haemolymph was diluted with saline, the incubation period was extended to 7 or 10 days. Once infected with the potato leaf-roll virus by injection, the aphids retained their infectivity. Serial transmissions were then carried out as follows. Viruliferous aphids were colonized on a virus-immune plant such as Chinese cabbage for 7 days; haemolymph from these aphids was then injected into a series of known virus-free aphids. After 7 days, the process was repeated, and this was carried out 15 times. At each passage the presence of the leaf-roll virus was demonstrated by feeding the aphids on susceptible plants. It is calculated that if no multiplication had taken place the dilution would have reached $10^{-21}$, while the actual dilution end-point of the virus in haemolymph is $10^{-4}$.

A second case of the apparent multiplication of a plant virus in an aphid has been described by Duffus (1963). The virus in question, causing the yellow-vein disease of sow thistle *Sonchus oleraceus*, is transmitted by the aphid *Amphorophora lactucae* (L.). The latent period in the insect is very long and transmission is independent of the quantity of virus ingested. The shortest insect-latent period recorded was 8 days at 25°C, the longest latent period was 46 days at 5°C. From experiments carried out on the incubation and latent periods in both the plant and the insect, it seems that a certain virus concentration must be built up in the aphid vector before transmission occurs. Aphids retain infectivity throughout their lives. The sow thistle yellow-vein virus (SYVV) is transmitted in essentially the same manner as those plant viruses which multiply in their leaf hopper vectors.

The only other plant virus known at present, with a similar long latent period in the aphid vector, i.e. 10 to 19 days, is that of strawberry crinkle (Prentice and Woollcombe, 1951).

There are several other specific relationships between aphids and viruses which can only be referred to briefly here.

One of these is the variation in transmission of a single virus by a single aphid species. As Rochow (1963) has pointed out in his review of aphid variations in virus transmission, there are three kinds of this variation in an aphid species: (*a*) among different *clones* of *strains*; (*b*) among various *developmental* stages; (*c*) among different *forms* of one species. Stubbs (1955), working with the yellows virus of spinach, a virus of the circulatory type, found considerable variation in the ability of different cultures of the aphid *Myzus persicae* to transmit the virus.

Another type of variation is illustrated by the transmission of cucumber mosaic virus by *Myzus persicae*. This is a stylet-borne virus and Badami (1958) has shown that a strain of the virus isolated from spinach lost its affinity with the aphid *M. persicae*, which is the usual vector, and could no longer be transmitted by it. This appears to be due to a change in the virus itself, because the aphid was still able to transmit other strains of cucumber mosaic virus, and the original strain of virus was still aphid-transmissible by other species such as *Aphis gossypii* and *Myzus ascalonicus*.

Barley yellow-dwarf virus of the circulative type affords another example of variation in transmission. There is a remarkable specialization among isolates of the virus and some of the aphids that transmit it. Direct comparison of three aphid species and different isolates of barley yellow-dwarf virus have shown the existence of at least three vector-specific strains of the virus. In discussing the basis for this specificity, Rochow (1963) suggests that the major basis for the variation lies in the virus rather than in the aphids. As to the mechanism controlling this specificity, it might be centred in any one, or a combination, of three main areas, i.e. acquisition of virus from the plant, physiology of virus in the aphid after acquisition, or inoculation of virus to plants by the aphid vector.

In the discussion on satellite viruses in Chapter Seven, it was pointed out how one virus may depend on another virus in the same plant for assistance in the performance of some function or other. In the case of the virus complex in tobacco known as 'rosette', one of the two components of the complex, the mottle virus, is dependent upon the presence in the plant of the other component, the vein-distorting virus, to enable it to be aphid-borne. At the moment no satisfactory explanation of this phenomenon is available.

*Jassidae, leafhoppers*

The relationship between plant viruses and leafhoppers and related insects is also somewhat varied, but the biological association seems more intimate than with the aphids.

One instance where transmission by a leafhopper approaches the stylet-borne type has been described by Ling (1966). The virus in question causes the 'tungro' disease of rice (*Oryza sativa* L.) and it is transmitted by the green leafhopper (*Nephotettix impicticeps*, Ishihara). Vectors that become infective transmit the virus immediately after acquisition feeding and no definite delay in the development of infective power in the vector could be demonstrated. If one does occur, it is of a duration less than 2 hours, since some virus-free vectors transmitted the tungro virus following acquisition- and inoculation-feeding periods of 1 hour each. The fact that the virus is lost by the vector after moulting indicates that it is not of the circulative type. However, it is somewhat differentiated from the stylet-borne category of viruses because it can be retained by some insects for as long as 5 days without recourse to a fresh source of virus.

The virus of sugar-beet curly-top has a slightly more intimate relationship with its leafhopper vector *Circulifer tenellus* (Baker), and can be regarded as a circulative virus since it is not lost by the insect after a moult. Furthermore, it can be retained by the leafhopper for 100 days, but the fact that the virus concentration gradually decreases indicates that no multiplication is taking place. (Freitag, 1936; Bennett and Wallace, 1938.)

It is in the leafhoppers that biological transmission, or, to use the current phraseology, the propagative type of relationship, is most highly developed. There are several methods for approaching the investigation of biological transmission, and they can be conveniently grouped as follows: (*a*) indirect experimental evidence; (*b*) transovarial transmission of virus; (*c*) interaction of related viruses in the insect; (*d*) effect of the virus on the vector; (*e*) visualization of the virus inside the body of the vector.

*Indirect Experimental Evidence.* A good deal of the early evidence on the multiplication of plant viruses in their leafhopper vectors was rather circumstantial and was open to other possible interpretations. Kunkel was a pioneer in studying this problem and laid the foundations for much of the later work. He worked principally with the virus of aster yellows and its vector *Macrosteles fascifrons*. In one experiment (Kunkel, 1937), viruliferous (virus-bearing) leafhoppers were exposed to a high temperature for varying lengths of time and were then transferred to young healthy aster plants. Subjected to a temperature of 36°C for 11 days or less, the insects still retained the power of infecting healthy asters, but the delay in development of infective power, or in other words the incubation period of the virus, increased with the duration of exposure to heat. The longer the insect was exposed to heat the longer it took to infect the plant. After 12 days' exposure, the insects lost their infectivity altogether, but could readily be made once more viruliferous by colonizing them on a fresh source of virus. Kunkel interpreted this as indicating a gradual loss of virus by the insect during the heat treatment;

the longer the exposure to heat the smaller the amount of viable virus left in the insect, and, in consequence, the longer the time necessary for this residual virus to multiply up sufficiently to give an infective dose.

Black (1941) approached the problem from a slightly different angle, since he had shown in 1940 that the virus of aster yellows could be inoculated successfully into the leafhopper vector, thus rendering it viruliferous. He colonized a large number of the leafhoppers on a yellowed aster plant for a given time and then removed all the insects to plants of rye, a species immune to the aster yellows virus. Thus, all the leafhoppers received approximately the same dose of virus. Next, after increasing intervals of time on the rye, a number of the insects were ground up into a paste, made into various dilutions, and inoculated into the alimentary canals of virus-free aster leafhoppers. This rather round-about method had to be employed because the aster yellows virus is not mechanically transmissible to its host plant. Black found that those leafhoppers which had been longest on the rye plants contained most virus, since they would withstand the highest dilutions and still produce infectivity in the inoculated leafhoppers, the inference being that the virus had multiplied most in those insects which had remained alive longest after the intake of virus in the first place.

A more direct method of measuring multiplication of a virus in an insect vector is by serial inoculation from insect to insect. This was first accomplished by Merrill and TenBroeck (1934) who demonstrated, by this method, the multiplication in the mosquito of the virus of equine encephalomyelitis. In 1952, Maramorosch made a similar serial passage-experiment and carried the aster yellows virus serially through ten groups of leafhoppers. He calculated that, if the virus was not multi-plying, the dilution at the tenth passage would have reached $10^{-40}$.

Two other yellows-type viruses have been tested in a similar manner. Black and Brakke (1952) transmitted the wound tumour virus through seven successive passages in the leafhopper *Agallia constricta*. This was calculated to equal a dilution of $10^{-18}$, although in actual dilution tests the wound tumour virus could not be recovered from insect juices at dilutions beyond $10^{-5}$.

The other virus, that of maize (= corn) stunt, was passed similarly through its insect vector, *Dalbulus maidis*. Serjeant (1967b) has injected virus-free individuals of the plant-hopper (*Delphacodes pellucida* Fabr.) with the virus of European wheat striate mosaic (EWSMV). After being injected at 5°C with extracts of either plants or hoppers, the insects infected plants with the virus but only after an interval of at least 8 days at 20 to 25°C. Nymphs fed on infected plants underwent a similar delay of 8 days before becoming viruliferous.

*Transovarial Transmission of Virus.* The first to demonstrate this was a Japanese worker Fukushi (1933) working with the dwarf disease of rice and its vector *Nephotettix apicalis* Motsch. He showed that the virus was transmitted from an infective parent insect to the offspring, but only through the female parent. Moreover, the progeny from such an infective parent did not itself become infective until after a period of 9 days from the date of hatching. Fukushi also showed that the virus could be passed through 6 generations involving 82 infective leaf-hoppers, and all derived from a single virus-bearing female without access to a further source of virus. This is strong indirect evidence of multiplication since otherwise the dilution of the virus involved would be too great.

Black (1950) carried out similar experiments to those of Fukushi, but using the virus of clover club-leaf, which he has shown to be transmitted through the egg of the vector, a leafhopper, *Agalliopsis novella* Say. From a pair of viruliferous leafhoppers the breeding was carried out through 21 generations over a period of 5 years. The insects were fed throughout on virus-immune lucerne plants without loss of infectivity. Black has calculated that, if multiplication of the virus is not assumed, the dilution of the original virus in the parent insect exceeded $1 : 2.8 \times 10^{26}$.

Since these original experiments, other examples of leafhopper-borne viruses that are transmitted transovarially have been discovered. For instance, the virus of rice stripe disease has been transmitted in this way through 40 generations of *Delphacodes striatella* (Fallen), a plant-hopper belonging to the Delphacidae (Shinkai, 1955). The same worker (Shinkai, 1960) demonstrated the transovarial transmission of rice dwarf virus through *Deltocephalus* (*Inazuma*) *dorsalis* Motsch., as well as through *Nephotettix cincticeps*, as originally shown by Fukushi.

For further examples of this phenomenon the reader is referred to a review by Maramorosch (1963).

*Interaction of Related Viruses in the Insect.* It has been shown in Chapter Three that in some cases one virus will inhibit the entrance of a related virus into the same plant; this is known as cross-protection. In one of his last experiments, Kunkel (1955) investigated the possibility of a similar interaction of viruses inside the leafhopper vector. He used two strains of aster yellows virus, the New York or type strain and a California strain. The difference between these two lay mainly in host range rather than in differences of symptomatology, so that the first problem was to find a plant that would react differentially to the two viruses. Two such plants were eventually found, the zinnia and the periwinkle, *Vinca rosea*; the latter was chosen as being easy to grow from cuttings and as being a favourite host of the leafhopper. On this plant, the California virus produced short, stubby, or swollen side shoots as compared to the thin, elongated shoots characteristic of the type virus. The next step was to ascertain whether these two strains would cross-protect against each other in the plant, and cross-infection experiments proved that this was the case.

In order to investigate whether a similar cross-protection existed in the insect, the following experiment was carried out. A colony consisting of about 30 virus-free young aster-leafhoppers was placed on an aster plant affected with the type strain of aster yellows and a similar colony was placed on an aster plant affected with California aster yellows. After 2 weeks, the colony that had fed on the plant with the type strain was placed on a plant affected with California aster yellows and vice versa. After a further 2 weeks both colonies were transferred individually to healthy young aster plants.

The results of this experiment showed that the virus transmitted was that on which the insects first fed. In other words, those insects which fed first on the type strain transmitted only that virus, and those which fed first on the California strain transmitted only the California virus. Thus, the strains of aster yellows virus cross-protect against each other in the insect as effectively as they do in the plant. It must be presumed, therefore, that multiplication of the first virus in the insect leaves no opportunity for multiplication of the second.

*Effect of the Virus on the Vector.* An important question is whether a plant virus which is thought to multiply in the insect vector has a deleterious effect on the insect. Is the vector itself diseased?

There seems to be no evidence suggesting that insect vectors in which animal viruses multiply are in any way adversely affected; the mosquito vector of equine encephalomyelitis virus is a case in point. But the same does not appear to be true of some plant viruses and their vectors. The first plant virus shown to be definitely injurious to the insect vector was that causing Western X-disease of stone fruits and a yellows disease of celery. This virus has been shown to cause a significant reduction in the life span of the vector *Colladonus montanus* Van Duzee (Jensen, 1958, 1959 a and b). Viruliferous individuals also produce fewer eggs than do noninfective controls (Jensen, 1962).

Moreover, when Western X-disease virus (WXV) is injected into the leafhopper vector, either by means of infective haemolymph, or by dilutions of whole insect extracts, it causes premature death. Mortality due to virus occurred earlier in injected insects than in those acquiring virus by feeding (Jensen *et al.*, 1967).

35 days after exposure of the leafhopper (*C. montanus*) to celery infected with WXV, or 26 days after injection with infectious extracts or haemolymph, histopathological symptoms could be detected in the leafhopper. Dark-staining neural lesions, confined to the perineurium, appeared earliest and were most conspicuous in stained sections of the optic lobes of the brain, but they occurred also in other parts of the brain and in the other cephalic and thoracic ganglia. The cytoplasm of the serous cells of the anterior lobe of the salivary glands became dense and dark staining. After 48 days many of the insects had died (Whitcomb *et al.*, 1967).

Incidentally, not all individuals of a given species of leafhopper vector are necessarily able to transmit the virus in question. Lamey *et al.* (1964) have made a study of the transmission of the 'Hoja blanca' virus to rice plants, and they find that a normal population of the vector *Sogata orizicola* Muir contains only 10 per cent of potential transmitters.

The effect generally of plant viruses on insects has been reviewed at some length by Jensen (1963). See also a review article on the harmful and beneficial effects of plant viruses on insects (Maramorosch and Jensen, 1963).

*Visualization of the Virus Inside the Body of the Vector.* Fukushi *et al.* (1962, 1963) were probably the first to visualize a plant virus inside the body of the insect vector by means of electron microscopy. They showed the virus of rice dwarf disease *in situ* in the abdomen of the vector *Nephotettix apicalis* var. *cincticeps.* The virus occurred in microcrystals in the cytoplasm of abdominal cells; it was not observed in cell nuclei or in mitochondria. It is interesting that the microcrystals of virus are somewhat reminiscent of an insect virus, the *Tipula* iridescent virus (TIV) (Smith, 1962); both occur in microcrystals in the cell cytoplasm of infected insects and both are icosahedra.

Shikata *et al.* (1964) have demonstrated similarly the presence of wound tumour virus in both the insect vector and the plant tumour. Virus particles, obtained from both insect and plant, appeared to be of similar size and morphology. The crystalline arrangement of the virus particles in the fatbody of the vector *Agallia constricta* is very like that of the virus of rice-dwarf disease in the abdomen of the insect vector.

Shikata *et al.* (1966) seem to have been the first to demonstrate visually a plant virus inside the body of an aphid vector (Plate 10). This is the virus of pea enation mosaic, but it is not yet known if this virus multiplies in the aphid.

In view of the evidence thus briefly reviewed, there can be little doubt that some plant viruses do multiply in their insect vectors. So are these plant or insect viruses? It may be significant that insects are associated in one way or another with three of the major groups of viruses, those attacking animals, insects, and plants.

## Vectors Outside the Insecta

### Eriophyidae: *Mites*

The first evidence of the transmission of plant viruses by mites is contained in an early paper on the 'reversion' disease of blackcurrant (*Ribes*). It was suggested that the vector was the 'big bud' mite *Phytoptus* (*Eriophyes*) *ribis* Westw. (Amos *et al.* 1927). A quarter of a century later this was confirmed by Massee (1952).

In addition to the virus of reversion, there are five other mite-transmitted viruses known and others are suspected. Three of these infect only grasses, i.e. wheat streak mosaic, wheat spot mosaic, and ryegrass mosaic; the other three affect only woody perennials and cause

PLATE 1. Plant of Chinese cabbage infected with the virus of turnip yellow mosaic. (A.R.C. Virus Research Unit, Cambridge.)

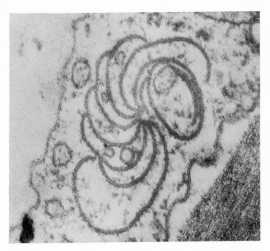

PLATE 2. 'Pin-wheel' type of intracellular inclusion induced by a long flexuous type of virus in the cells of the sunflower *Helianthus annuus*. (H. J. Arnott and K. M. Smith, 1967.) (× 110,000)

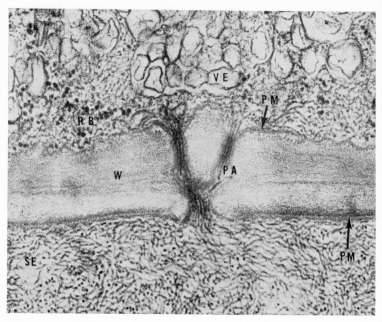

PLATE 3. Longitudinal section of parenchyma cell (*above*) and sieve element (SE, *below*) of small vein from *Beta vulgaris* leaf infected with beet yellows. Wall (W) between the two cells bears a branched plasmodesma containing virus particles (PA). Vesicles (VE) and ribosomes (RB) present in parenchyma cell, absent in sieve element. Details: PA, beet yellows virus particles; PM, plasma membrane; RB, ribosomes; SE sieve element; VE, vesicles associated with beet yellows infection; W, cell wall. (K.Esau, J. Cronshaw, and L. L. Hoefert, 1967.) (×56,000)

PLATE 4. Tobacco rattle virus – picture obtained on an enlarger which permits the subtraction of parts of the diffraction spectrum. In this case some of the 'noise' was eliminated while passing the helical elements. (A.R.C. Virus Research Unit, Cambridge.) (× 700,000)

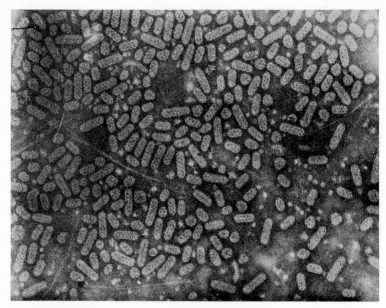
PLATE 5. Electron micrograph of unfractionated preparation of lucerne (alfalfa) mosaic virus, fixed in formalin and mounted in phosphotungstate. (A. J. Gibbs, H. L. Nixon, and R. D. Woods, 1963.) (×60,000)

PLATE 6. Photograph of a model of the lucerne (alfalfa) mosaic virus particle, showing the interlocking rings of six knobs on the surface. (A. J. Gibbs, H. L. Nixon, and R. D. Woods, 1963.)

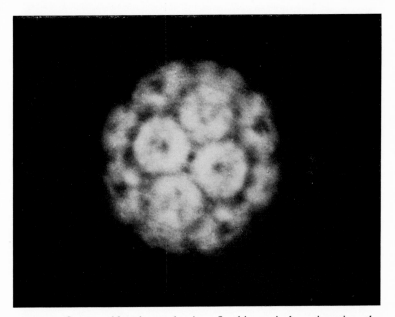

PLATE 7. Cowpea chlorotic mottle virus. In this particular orientation, the structures of the upper and lower sides reinforce to give an image having a four-fold redundacy of detail, which was also employed in the photographic reconstruction of the virus particle. (A.R.C. Virus Research Unit, Cambridge.) ($\times$ 2,000,000)

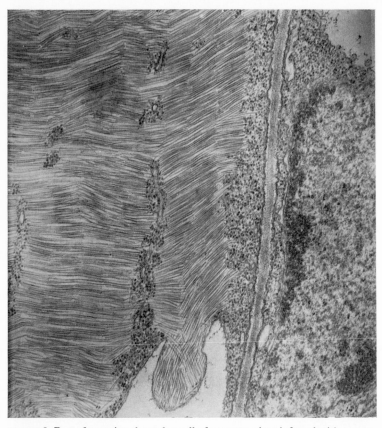

PLATE 8. Part of a section through a cell of a tomato plant infected with tomato (=tobacco mosaic virus): note the regular arrangement of the virus particles which are aligned end to end. (×26,000)

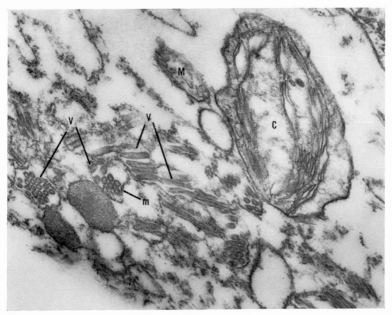

PLATE 9. Mesophyll cell of *Nicotiana* infected with lettuce necrotic yellows virus, tissue was taken from a young systemically infected leaf: V, virus particles; C, chloroplast; M, mitochondrion; m, membrane around bundles of virus particles. (T. C. Chambers, N. C. Crowley, and R. I. B. Francki, 1965.) (× 12,000 ×2·5)

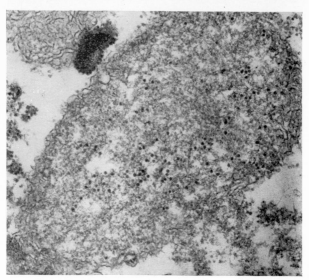

PLATE 10. Section through the dissected gut of a viruliferous aphid with an accumulation of pea enation mosaic virus particles in the lumen. Note also accumulation of virus particles around an electron dense area and at bottom of photograph. (E. Shikata, K. Maramorosch, and R. R. Granados, 1966.) (×18,000)

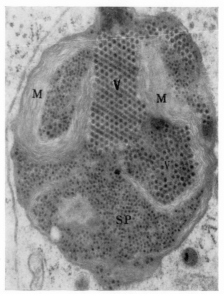

PLATE 11. The virus of rice dwarf disease (V) arranged in crystalline and ir-regular array, smaller particles (SP), and multiple membranes (M) within the intracytoplasmic dense area of the mycetome of a viruliferous leafhopper *Nephotettix cincticeps*. (after Nasu, *in* C. Matsui and A. Yamaguchi, 1966.) (×20,000)

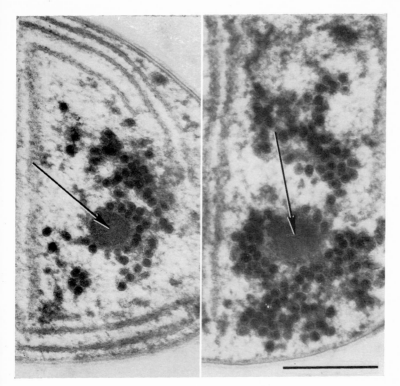

PLATE 12. Sections of two cells of the blue-green alga, *Plectonema boryanum*, showing numbers of mature virus particles in the virogenic stroma: arrows mark the 'polyhedral body'. Compare with Plate 13. (K. M. Smith, R. M. Brown, P. Walne, and D. A. Goldstein, 1966.) (bar = 1μ)

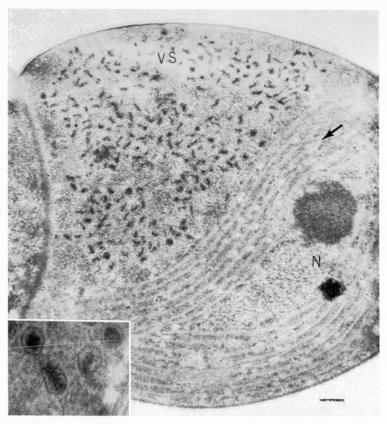

PLATE 13. Section through a cell of *Plectonema boryanum* 1 hour after infection: VS, virogenic stroma; N, nucleoplasm. Note the numerous helices in the virogenic stroma. The inset shows two helices – one partially, the other completely, inside the outer membrane. (K. M. Smith, R. M. Brown, and P. Walne, 1967.) (bar = 100 mμ; inset × 109,000)

PLATE 14. Cabbage black ringspot virus on tobacco; an example of local lesions. (A.R.C. Virus Research Unit, Cambridge.)

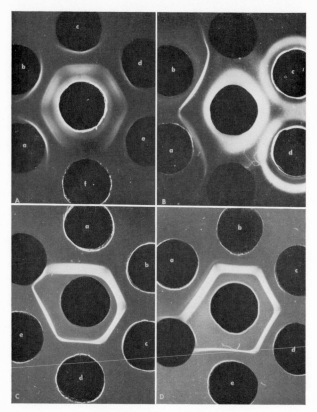

PLATE 15. (A) Central well filled with antiserum to potato virus X. Well *a* contains sap of *N. tabacum* plants infected with potato virus X; *b, c, d,* and *e* contain a series of twofold dilutions of the preparation used in *a*; *f* contains fraction 1 protein. Note the progressive disappearance of the band caused by virus particles with increasing dilution. The second band nearer to the middle well is caused by virus breakdown products or soluble antigens. (B) Central well filled with grapevine fanleaf virus (GFV) antiserum. Well *a* contains 1 mg/ml purified GFV; *b,* 4 mg/ml purified GFV, note the enhanced visibility of the precipitate at optimal proportions (well *b*); wells *c* and *d* contain crude sap from healthy grapevine plants, illustrating nonspecific precipitation. (C) Centre well filled with antiserum to fraction 1 protein of *Cucurbita pepo* (titre 1/128). Wells *a–e* contain a series of twofold dilutions of crude sap of a healthy narrow plant; note position of narrowest band formed near optimal proportions opposite well *d*. (D) Centre well filled with alfalfa mosaic virus (AMV) antiserum. Wells *a–e* contain a series of twofold dilutions of a purified preparation of AMV. (M. H. V. van Regenmortel, 1966.)

peach mosaic, fig mosaic, and, as already mentioned, blackcurrant reversion.

All the mite vectors, so far identified, belong to the same group, the Eriophyidae, which seems to be distinct from other phytophagous mites (Keifer, 1952).

The vector of wheat streak mosaic virus (WSMV) is *Aceria tulipae* Keifer; this virus is easily transmissible by sap-inoculation (Slykhuis, 1953, 1955). The second virus disease of wheat, called wheat spot mosaic (WSpMV), is transmitted by the same species of mite, with the difference that this virus is not sap-transmissible and is retained by the mite for 12 days without further access to a source of virus (Slykhuis, 1956). A single mite can carry both WSMV and WSpMV at the same time.

The third virus of this group causes a mosaic disease of rye grass and has been studied by Mulligan (1960). The mite vector of this disease is *Abacarus hystrix* (Nalepa), and although it occurs commonly on wheat it is unable to transmit WSMV or WSpMV. Ryegrass mosaic virus (RMV) is easily sap-transmissible.

The first tree virus shown to be transmitted by a mite was that of fig mosaic (Flock and Wallace, 1955, 1956). The vector is the fig mite *Aceria ficus* (Cotte). As Slykhuis points out, it is not surprising that fig mosaic is so widely spread, since the host plant is a perennial and the mite is an efficient and abundant vector. It was shown in tests that a single viruliferous mite per test plant infected 7 out of 10 plants.

The vector of the virus causing peach mosaic had been sought for many years and various sucking insects, which frequent peach trees, such as aphids and leafhoppers had been tested without success. Then, in 1955, Wilson *et al.* identified the vector as the mite *Eriophyes insidiosus*. Other species of mites commonly found on diseased peach trees such as *Vasates cornutus* failed to transmit the virus.

None of the mite-transmitted viruses affecting woody plants appear to be sap-transmissible. There is some evidence of a biological relationship between some of these viruses and their mite vectors. Slykhuis (1962) points out that each virus is specifically transmitted by only one mite species even though other species may be present on the same host. Of the six mite-transmitted viruses known, only two, WSMV and RMV, are sap-transmissible. RMV seems to be similar to the stylet-borne

G

aphid-transmitted viruses in that infectivity is lost by the mite within
24 hours after removal from the source of virus. On the other hand,
WSMV has been found to persist in its vector for 9 days, WSpMV for
12 days, and peach mosaic virus for 2 days, after removal from their
diseased hosts. None of the mite-transmitted viruses appear to be passed
transovarially to the offspring, but WSMV and WSpMV persist in the
mite *A tulipae* through the moults.

In the insect-transmission of the virus of tomato spotted wilt, the
vector, a thrips, is unable to pick up the virus *de novo*; it can only transmit the virus if acquired during the nymphal stage (Samuel *et al.*, 1930).
A similar state of affairs exists with WSMV where the nymphs of the
mite *A. tulipae* acquire the virus but the adults do not (Slykhuis, 1962).
There seems to be no satisfactory explanation of this phenomenon at
present.

The subject of mite-transmission of plant viruses has been reviewed
by Slykhuis (1965).

*Nematoda, eelworms*

Some years ago a new virus disease appeared in an insect-proof glasshouse at Cambridge affecting a plant of Rock Cress, *Arabis hirsuta*, and
was called *Arabis* mosaic (Smith and Markham, 1944). The virus of
*Arabis* mosaic has now been identified as the same as, or closely related
to, a number of soil-borne viruses which have been described affecting
the vine, the cherry, the strawberry, and the raspberry; these viruses
are all transmitted by the dagger nematode worms, various species of
the one genus Xiphinema.

Sixteen species of nematodes have so far been incriminated as vectors
of plant viruses.

In his review of the biology of soil-borne viruses, Cadman (1963)
divides them into two groups, those transmitted by plant parasitic
nematodes he calls *Nepoviruses*. The second group contains viruses
which are transmitted by Chytrid fungi; these are discussed in the next
section. This difference in the mode of transmission of soil-borne viruses
is reflected sharply in the time that soils containing the viruses remain
infective. Soils containing nematode-transmitted viruses lose infectivity
rapidly and permanently when allowed to dry for a week or more at
20°C. On the other hand, soils containing fungus-borne viruses remain

infective after storage for years in the dry state. This, of course, is not a property of the viruses *in vitro*, as Cadman points out, but lies rather in the capacity of the vectors, nematode worm or fungal spore, to withstand desiccation.

The first demonstration that eelworms were capable of transmitting plant viruses was made by Hewitt *et al.* (1958). They showed that the 'fanleaf disease' of grapevines was spread by the eelworm *Xiphinema index*. The distribution of fanleaf disease is very wide, it occurs commonly in California and is widespread in Europe, where it is known under a variety of names, roncet, court noué, reisigkrankheit, etc.

Hewitt and his co-workers have investigated some of the relationships between the fanleaf virus and *X. index*. Preliminary experiments suggest that the time necessary for the eelworm to acquire the virus (acquisition feed) is comparatively short, but, on the other hand, the period during which the eelworm remains infective (viruliferous) without access to a further source of virus may be as long as 30 days. All developmental stages of the nematode seem capable of virus transmission and there is no evidence of transovarial passage of the virus.

Some information is available on the relationships between tobacco ringspot virus (TRSV) and the eelworm vector *Xiphinema americanum*. Eelworms become viruliferous 8 to 24 hours after having access to an infected plant. Viruliferous individuals of *X. americanum*, after being stored in soil at 10°C for 49 weeks, were still able to transmit TRSV to 60 per cent of the indicator plants (Bergeson and Athow, 1963). This may seem incompatible with the statement above that soil containing nematode-borne viruses rapidly loses infectivity on storing. It should be noted, however, that during the period of 49 weeks, during which *X. americanum* remained infective, the soil was not allowed to dry out and the nematodes were still living. McGuire (1964) has studied the efficiency of the eelworm *X. americanum* as a vector of tobacco ringspot virus to young cucumber plants. He found that TRSV could be transmitted by a single eelworm, but percentages of infected plants increased with an increase in the number of nematodes. There seemed to be no difference in transmitting power between larvae and adults since four developmental stages tested all transmitted the virus. Single nematodes acquired TRSV within 24 hours, the shortest acquisition-feeding time tested. Symptoms of virus infection usually appeared in 13 to 25 days in the leaves of plants to which transmission had been effected.

It seems clear that a biological relationship of some kind must exist between virus and eelworm in some cases. The following facts support this; not every species of plant-feeding nematode can transmit virus, and the eelworm can retain virus for long periods. Furthermore, there are specific nematode vectors for serologically distinctive forms of raspberry ringspot and tomato black ring viruses (Harrison, 1964).

The list of eelworm-transmitted viruses is now very long and is likely to be increased; thus, the group of ringspot viruses, so-called from a common symptom on certain herbaceous hosts, includes tomato blackring, tomato ringspot, raspberry ringspot, arabis mosaic, cherry rosette, and peach yellow bud mosaic (the last-named has recently been shown by Cadman to be serologically related to tomato ringspot virus).

Strains of tomato black-ring virus have been described under different names in different countries. The original, or type strain, was described in England by Smith (1946), the potato 'bouquet' strain from German potato crops (Köhler, 1952), the beet ringspot strain from sugar-beet, potato, turnip, oat, raspberry, strawberry, and weed plants in Scotland (Harrison, 1957, 1958), and lettuce ringspot (Smith and Short, 1959).

The biology of soil-borne viruses has been reviewed by Harrison (1960) and by Cadman (1963).

### Chytrid Fungi

*Olpidium brassicae.* The first virus of tobacco necrosis (TNV) was discovered by Smith and Bald (1935) and it was later pointed out by Bawden and Pirie (1942) that there existed several such viruses, biologically similar but serologically unrelated. They form an interesting group of soil-borne viruses, and, until recently, there has been much speculation on their mode of transmission.

These viruses infect the roots of many plant species without becoming systemic in their hosts; exceptions to this rule are beans (*Phaseolus vulgaris*) and tulips in which systemic diseases are produced.

In the past it had been suggested that a root fungus might be the vector, but the first circumstantial evidence of this was presented by Teakle (1960) and by Teakle and Yarwood (1962), who showed that the fungus *Olpidium brassicae* was closely associated with infection of plants by one of the TNV group.

Teakle (1962) carried out a number of experiments which seemed to prove that *Olpidium* does in fact transmit TNV. Thus TNV infection of roots was induced only when actively swimming *Olpidium* zoospores were able to encyst on the roots of mung bean seedlings (*Phaseolus mungo* L.) in the presence of TNV. Mild treatments which inactivated the zoospores prevented TNV infection of plants.

Evidence suggests that certain strains of *Olpidium brassicae* transmit TNV with great regularity, whereas others fail to do so. Teakle reports that several crucifer strains of *Olpidium brassicae* have not transmitted TNV but lettuce strains have consistently done so. Teakle and Gold (1963) have demonstrated that virus transmission is not just a question of surface contamination; the *Olpidium* spore acquires and harbours TNV and so is a genuine vector. Thus, it was found that when dilutions of TNV and its antiserum were mixed and added to zoospores released into water, no virus transmission to roots resulted from the mixture, but transmission was achieved when zoospores were released from roots into the virus suspension and the antiserum added later. Again, the addition of TNV antiserum to roots bearing zoospores that had encysted on the roots in the presence of TNV did not prevent TNV infection, although the antiserum inactivated the virus in suspension.

Some recent work by Fry and Campbell (1966) gives details of the relationships between the fungus, the virus, and the roots of the host. Additional evidence that *Olpidium* actually is the vector was provided by two types of experiments. When suspensions of *Olpidium* and TNV were filtered so as to remove all zoospores, the filtrate which still contained infective TNV was non-infective to the plant. Investigation also showed that *Olpidium* and TNV infected the same parts of lettuce roots.

Experiments on the susceptibility of lettuce roots to infection showed that roots of 3- or 7-day-old lettuce plants were more susceptible to both *Olpidium* and TNV than roots of 12- or 19-day-old plants. There was also a difference in susceptibility in lettuce varieties to infection by *Olpidium*; TNV infection decreased *Olpidium* reproduction more in the necrotic-reacting variety 'Climax' than in the non-necrotic reacting variety 'Dark Green Cos'. TNV could be transmitted by as few as

58 *Olpidium* zoospores per millilitre; with about $10^5$ zoospores per millilitre, TNV was transmitted from solutions so dilute as to give no lesions when rubbed on the leaves of *Phaseolus vulgaris* L.

Another virus transmitted by *Olpidium brassicae* is that of 'lettuce big-vein'. At one time it was considered that this disease was caused by TNV, because of the frequent presence of this virus in the roots of lettuce affected with big-vein, but it is now known that a separate independent virus is involved. It is thought that *Olpidium brassicae* carries the virus of lettuce big-vein internally in the zoospores, as well as within resting sporangia, and that exchange of the virus from fungus to host or from host to fungus occurs during the early stages of infection (Campbell and Grogan, 1963, 1964).

There is a good deal of circumstantial evidence that the virus of tomato bushy stunt (TBSV) is soil-borne, probably by a Chytrid fungus (Lovisolo *et al.*, 1965).

For a general account of the transmission of plant viruses by Chytrid fungi the reader is referred to a review by Grogan and Campbell (1966).

**References**

AMOS, J., HATTON, R. G., KNIGHT, R. C., and MASSEE, A. M. (1927) *Ann. Rept. East Malling Res. Sta. Kent.* **13**, 126–50.

BADAMI, R. S. (1958) *Ann. appl. Biol.* **46**, 554–62.

BAWDEN, F. C. and PIRIE, N. W. (1942) *Brit. J. exp. Path.* **23**, 314.

BENNETT, C. W. and WALLACE, H. E. (1938) *J. Agr. Res.* **56**, 31–51.

BERGESON, G. B. and ATHOW, K. L. (1963) *Phytopathology.* **53**, 871 (Abstr.).

BLACK, L. M. (1941) *Phytopathology.* **31**, 120.

BLACK, L. M. (1950) *Nature.* **166**, 852–3.

BLACK, L. M. and BRAKKE, M. K. (1952) *Phytopathology.* **42**, 269–73.

BRADLEY, R. H. E. (1952) *Ann. appl. Biol.* **39**, 78.

BRADLEY, R. H. E. (1959) *Proc. 7th Internat. Botan. Congr.* 1960. Montreal.

CADMAN, C. H. (1963) *Ann. Rev. Phytopathol.* **1**, 143–72.

CAMPBELL, R. N. and COLT, W. M. (1967) *Phytopathology.* **57**, 502–4.

CAMPBELL, R. N. and GROGAN, R. G. (1963) *Phytopathology.* **53**, 252–9.

CAMPBELL, R. N. and GROGAN, R. G. (1964) *Phytopathology.* **54**, 681–90.

CHAUDHURI, R. P. (1950) *Ann. appl. Biol.* **37**, 342.

DAY, M. F. (1955) *Exptl. Parasitol.* **4**, 387.

DAY, M. F. and IRZYKIEWICZ, H. (1954) *Australian J. Biol. Sci.* **7**, 251.

DUFFUS, J. E. (1963) *Virology.* **21**, 194–202.

FLOCK, R. A. and WALLACE, J. M. (1955) *Phytopathology.* **45**, 52–4.

FLOCK, R. A. and WALLACE, J. M. (1956) *Calif. Agr.* **11**, 12.

FREITAG, J. H. (1936) *Hilgardia.* **10**, 305–42.

FRY, P. R. and CAMPBELL, R. N. (1966) *Virology.* **30**, 517–27.

FUKUSHI, T. (1933) *Proc. Imp. Acad. (Tokyo).* **9**, 451.

FUKUSHI, T. and SHIKATA, E. (1963) *Virology.* **21**, 503.

FUKUSHI, T., SHIKATA, E., and KIMURA, I. (1962) *Virology.* **18**, 192–205.

GROGAN, R. C. and CAMPBELL, R. N. (1966) *Ann. Rev. Phytopathol.* **4**, 29–52.

HARRISON, B. D. (1957) *Ann. appl. Biol.* **45**, 462.

HARRISON, B. D. (1958) *J. Gen. Microbiol.* **18**, 450.

HARRISON, B. D. (1960) *Adv. Vir. Res.* **7**, 131.

HARRISON, B. D. (1964) *Virology.* **22**, 544.

HEINZE, K. (1955) *Phytopathol. Z.* **25**, 103.

HEWITT, W. B., RASKI, D. J., and GOHEEN, A. C., (1958) *Phytopathology.* **48**, 586.

JENSEN, D. D. (1958) *Phytopathology.* **48**, 394 (Abstr.).

JENSEN, D. D. (1959a) *Virology.* **8**, 164–75.

JENSEN, D. D. (1959b) *Pan-Pacific Entomologist.* **35**, 65–82.

JENSEN, D. D. (1962) *Proc. 11th Internat. Congr. Entomol.* 1960. Vienna. pp. 790–1.

JENSEN, D. D. (1963) *Ann. N. Y. Acad. Sci.* **105**, 685–712.

JENSEN, D. D., WHITCOMB, R. F., and RICHARDSON, J. (1967) *Virology* **31**, 532–8.

KEIFER, H. H. (1952) *Bull. Calif. Insect Survey.* **2**, No. 1.

KENNEDY, J. S., DAY, M. F., and EASTOP, V. F. (1962) *A Conspectus of Aphids as Vectors of Plant Viruses.* 114 pp. London: Commonwealth Inst. Entomol.

KÖHLER, E. (1952) *Phytopathol. Z.* **19**, 284.

KUNKEL, L. O. (1937) *Am. J. Botany.* **24**, 316.

KUNKEL, L. O. (1955) *Adv. Vir. Res.* **3**, 251.

LAMEY, H. A. HENDRICK, R. D., EVERETT, T. R., and SHOWERS, W. B. (1964) *Phytopathology.* **54**, 624 (Abstr.).

LING, K. C. (1966) *Phytopathology.* **56**, 1252–6.

LOVISOLO, O., BODE, O., and VOLK, J. (1965) *Phytopathol. Z.* **53**, Heft 4, 323–42.

MARAMOROSCH, K. (1963) *Ann. Rev. Entomol.* **8**, 369–414.

MARAMOROSCH, K. and JENSEN, D. D. (1963) *Ann. Rev. Microbiol.* **17**, 495–530.

MARKHAM, R. and SMITH, K. M. (1949) *Parasitology.* **39**, 330–42.

MASSEE, A. M. (1952) *Ann. Rept. East Malling Res. Sta. Kent* 1951. pp. 162–5.

MCGUIRE, M. C. (1964) *Phytopathology.* **54**, 799–801.

MERRILL, H. M. and TENBROECK, C. (1934) *Proc. Soc. exp. Biol. N.Y.* **32**, 421.

MULLIGAN, T. (1960) *Ann. appl. Biol.* **48**, 575–9.

NAULT, L. R., GYRISCO, G. C., and ROCHOW, W. F. (1964) *Phytopathology.* **54**, 1269–72.

ORLOB, G. B. (1963) *Phytopathology.* **53**, 822–30.

OSBORN, H. T. (1935) *Phytopathology.* **25**, 160.

PIRONE, T. P. (1967) *Virology.* **31**, 569–71.

PRENTICE, I. W. and WOOLLCOMBE, T. M. (1951) *Ann. appl. Biol.* **33**, 50.

ROCHOW, W. F. (1963) *Ann. N.Y. Acad. Sci.* **105**, 713–29.

SAMUEL, G., BALD, J. G., and PITTMAN, H. A. (1930) *Australia Commonwealth Council Sci. Ind. Res. Bull.* No. 44.

SERJEANT, E. P. (1967a) *Ann. appl. Biol.* **59**, 31–8.

SERJEANT, E. P. (1967b) *Ann. appl. Biol.* **59**, 39–48.

SHIKATA, E., MARAMOROSCH, K., and GRANADOS, R. R. (1966) *Virology.* **29**, 426–36.

SHIKATA, E., ORENSKI, S. W., HIRUMI, H., MITSUHASHI, J., and MARAMOROSCH, K. (1964) *Virology.* **23**, 441–4.

SHINKAI, A. (1955) *Ann. Rept. Kanto Tosan Phytopathol. Entomol. Soc.* (in Japanese) pp. 5–6.

SHINKAI, A. (1960) *Plant Protect.* (in Japanese) **14**, 146–50.

SIMONS, J. N. (1954) *Phytopathology.* **44**, 282.

SLYKHUIS, J. T. (1953) *Can. J. Agr. Sci.* **33**, 195–7.

SLYKHUIS, J. T. (1955) *Phytopathology.* **45**, 116–28.

SLYKHUIS, J. T. (1956) *Phytopathology.* **46**, 682–7.

SLYKHUIS, J. T. (1962) in *Biological Transmission of Disease Agents.* Ed. K. Maramorosch. pp. 41–61. New York: Academic Press.

SLYKHUIS, J. T. (1965) *Adv. Vir. Res.* **11**, 97–137.

SMITH, K. M. (1931) *Ann. appl. Biol.* **18**, 141.

SMITH, K. M. (1946) *Parasitology.* **37**, 126.

SMITH, K. M. (1962) *Adv. Vir. Res.* **9**, 195–240.

SMITH, K. M. (1965) *Adv. Vir. Res.* **11**, 61–96.

SMITH, K. M. and BALD, J. G. (1935) *Parasitology.* **27**, 231.

SMITH, K. M. and MARKHAM, R. (1944) *Phytopathology.* **34**, 324.

SMITH, K. M. and SHORT, M. E. (1959) *Plant Pathol.* **8**, 54–6.

STEGWEE, D. and PONSEN, M. B. (1958) *Entomol. Exptl. Appl.* **1**, 291.

STUBBS, L. L. (1955) *Australian J. Biol. Sci.* **8**, 68–74.

SYLVESTER, E. S. (1954) *Hilgardia.* **23**, 53.

SYLVESTER, E. S. (1962) in *Biological Transmission of Disease Agents.* Ed. K. Maramorosch. pp. 11–31. New York: Academic Press.

TEAKLE, D. S. (1960) *Nature.* **188**, 431–2.

TEAKLE, D. S. (1962) *Virology.* **18**, 224–31.

TEAKLE, D. S. and GOLD, A. H. (1963) *Virology.* **19**, 310–15.

TEAKLE, D. S. and YARWOOD, C. E. (1962) *Phytopathology.* **52**, 366 (Abstr.).

TOKO, H. V. and BRUEHL, G. W. (1959) *Phytopathology.* **49,** 343–7.

WANT, VAN DER, J. P. H. (1954) *Onderzoekingen over Virusziekten van der Boon (Phaseolus vulgaris).* 6 pp. Wageningen: Veenman and Zonen.

WALTERS, H. J. (1952) *Phytopathology.* **42, 355.**

WATSON, M. A. (1936) *Phil. Trans. Roy. Soc. London. B.* **226,** 457.

WATSON, M. A. and ROBERTS, F. M. (1939) *Proc. Roy. Soc. B.* **127,** 543.

WHITCOMB, R. F., JENSEN, D. D., AND RICHARDSON, J. (1967) *Virology.* **31,** 539–49.

WILSON, N. S., JONES, L. S., and COCHRAN, L. C. (1955) *Plant Disease Reptr.* **39,** 889–92.

# CHAPTER NINE

# Transmission other than by Vectors

There are several methods by which plant viruses can be transmitted from diseased to healthy hosts where there is no involvement with another organism. These methods, which include both natural and artificial means of transfer, are as follows: (*a*) mechanical inoculation; (*b*) grafting; (*c*) vegetative propagation; (*d*) seed transmission. The first two are largely artificial, the last two are natural, methods of spread.

## Mechanical Inoculation

Although improvements in techniques have rendered many viruses sap-transmissible, which could not earlier have been spread by these methods, it must be realized that there are still many not amenable to mechanical transmission. These are mostly viruses of the circulatory and propagative types which depend on specific insect vectors for their spread.

The word inoculation is used here in the restricted sense of the application of virus-bearing fluids to the tissues of susceptible plants. In the early days of plant virus study, the standard method of inoculating plants with viruses was to place a few drops of crude, extracted sap from the virus-infected plant upon the leaves of the plant to be infected and to scratch through the drop with a needle mounted in a handle. It was later discovered that the virus needed a wound, however slight – a broken trichome would suffice – to enable it to enter the cell, and therefore the more points of entry for the virus the better. Furthermore, it has been calculated that a very large number of virus particles must be applied to a leaf surface before a single virus lesion is formed (Chester, 1935; Bawden, 1950). Steere (1955) considers that only one particle out of 50,000 produces an infection. Nevertheless, it has been suggested by Kunkel (1934) and by Lauffer and Price (1945) that each lesion of tobacco mosaic is caused by a single virus particle. It is clear therefore that, at the best, mechanical inoculation is an indifferent mode of virus transmission. In efforts to improve it, a great many modifications have been evolved and these will be briefly described.

A great improvement in the inoculation technique was made by Samuel (1931), who showed that a gentle rubbing, almost a wiping, of the leaf to be inoculated gave a much higher infection percentage than the old needle method. A glass spatula, with a ground-glass face, dipped into the inoculum was recommended, the leaf to be inoculated being supported on a filter paper held in the hand. In practice, however, the tip of the forefinger or a piece of cheesecloth serve the purpose of a spatula equally well.

A further advance was made when it was found that an abrasive, dusted lightly over the leaves before inoculation or added to the inoculum, greatly increased the points of entry of the virus (Rawlins and Tompkins, 1936). A fine grade of carborundum powder or diatomaceous earth such as celite are suitable for this purpose. It is important, however, to dust the leaves lightly and to use the minimum of pressure while rubbing the leaves. Certain species of plants, notably French beans (*Phaseolus vulgaris*) and cowpea (*Vigna sinensis*), are particularly liable to be damaged by the inoculation process.

In 1929, Holmes demonstrated that, if the inoculated leaves were washed with water immediately after inoculation, under a tap or by means of a 'squash' bottle, the number of local lesions or points of entry of the virus was greater than if the leaves were left unwashed after inoculation.

If unduly prolonged, however, the washing may result in a decrease in infection. A 1-minute rinse may cause as much as 75 per cent decrease in infection with tobacco mosaic virus (Dale, 1956). Yarwood (1955) considers that a *short* washing of inoculated leaves immediately after inoculation increases infection, but reduces it if prolonged for more than 20 seconds.

To summarize, the routine inoculation of a fairly infectious sap-transmissible virus would be carried out as follows: dust the leaves to be inoculated *lightly* with celite or fine carborundum powder; dip the forefinger or a piece of muslin into the inoculum and rub the leaves *gently*; then rapidly wash the excess inoculum off the leaf surface.

Many modifications and special methods have been introduced for dealing with unstable viruses or those difficult to transmit mechanically. In addition, it has been shown that special treatment of plants before and after inoculation may have considerable influence on the reaction of the plants to infection.

Some alternative inoculation methods are sometimes useful. Taka-hashi (1947) and Yarwood (1952) used a stiff poster brush for inoculation. The latter dusted the leaves with carborundum and then applied a virus-water solution to the carborundum-dusted surface by means of a brush. This method gave 828 lesions on halves of leaves inoculated with the stiff poster brush, compared to 154 on those inoculated by means of the finger. Yarwood (1957a) has developed this technique further, into a brush-extraction method for virus transmission; a method especially suitable for plants with hairy leaves. When the stiff poster brush was stroked over the surface of a hairy leaf of a virus-infected plant and then over the leaf of a healthy susceptible plant, a high level of infection usually resulted.

The method was successful with the viruses of tobacco mosaic, tobacco ringspot, tomato spotted wilt, and alfalfa (lucerne) mosaic. The use of carborundum increased the efficiency of the method in all cases. If the leaves of the virus-infected plant were not hairy, the amount of virus obtained for inoculation could be increased if the brush was applied sufficiently hard to break the epidermis. This method is rapid and allows the virus to be taken from either the upper or the lower epidermis at will.

In cases where the virus is unstable and liable to rapid inactivation when the sap is extracted from the plant, a quick dry method of inoculation is preferable to the more conventional technique. This consists in rubbing the cut edges of leaf discs from the infected plant over the leaves of the healthy plant, which have previously been dusted with carborundum or sprayed with potassium monohydrogen phosphate. One or more discs may be used at a time, the optimum being four; the discs should be put together and trimmed to a straight edge. This method has proved successful with such viruses as those of tomato spotted wilt and apple mosaic on bean (*Phaseolus vulgaris*) (Yarwood, 1953).

For large-scale inoculation, it is sometimes possible to infect plants by means of a high-pressure spraying machine containing infective sap and carborundum powder (McKinney and Fellowes, 1951).

An artist's air brush has been used by Lindner and Kirkpatrick (1959); this lends itself to close standardization of pressure, fineness of spray, and distance from leaf surface.

Pricking and injection methods are still useful in the case of a few viruses which are confined to the phloem, such as those of sugar-beet curly-top, sugar-cane mosaic, etc.

*Preparation of Virus Inoculum*

The routine method of preparing the inoculum consists in grinding the virus-infected leaves with a pestle and mortar; if a large quantity of inoculum is required, an ordinary mincing machine may be used. The macerated leaf material is then placed in a piece of cheesecloth and the sap is extracted by pressure with the fingers or the pestle. If a large amount of material is involved, a screw press may be used.

Yarwood (1957) describes a method applicable to viruses such as tobacco mosaic virus which occur in high concentration in the infected plant. He adds about $1 cm^2$ of leaf tissue and about 3 drops of water to an ordinary mortar, grinds it thoroughly, and dilutes with additional water or phosphate solution as desired. This gives a suspension in which particulate matter is barely detectable with the unaided eye.

When only a very small quantity of inoculum is available, other methods can be used. Holmes (1952) suggests cutting out, with a cork borer, a small disc of leaf tissue, containing a single virus lesion if necessary, and grinding the disc between two pot labels.

The macerated tissue can then be transferred to a microscope slide with a ground glass surface and macerated further with a spatula which has a similar surface.

*Chemical Treatment of Inoculum*

Some viruses, such as that of tomato spotted wilt, are rapidly inactivated by oxidation when in expressed sap and are thus rather difficult to transmit by mechanical inoculation. Addition of sodium sulphite, $Na_2SO_3$, to the extracted sap retards oxidation, by reason of a reducing action, and prolongs the viability of the virus (Bald and Samuel, 1934; Ainsworth, 1936).

Similarly, the use of phosphate, by increasing the suceptibility of the leaves of beans, also greatly increases the percentage of successful virus transmissions (Yarwood, 1952). However, phosphate must be used with caution when inoculating bean leaves (*Phaseolus vulgaris*) with virus. Solutions of $K_2HPO_4$ can be injurious and the injury increases with increasing time of exposure and concentration. The addition of 1 per cent $K_2HPO_4$ to the inoculum increases the number of local lesions formed on bean leaves with the viruses of tobacco mosaic, tobacco necrosis, alfalfa mosaic, white clover mosaic, cucumber mosaic, pea mosaic, and cabbage black ringspot. With other viruses and on other host plants, the effect of the phosphate was much less (Yarwood, 1952).

Fulton (1957) describes a rapid method for the successful transmission of some unstable viruses from stone fruits. He obtained clear infective preparations by grinding the infected tissue with about twice its volume of calcium phosphate paste in 0·03M phosphate buffer and centrifuging for 1 minute or less. Infectivity of the supernatant was equal to or greater than that of untreated extracts and remained infective much longer. The method is effective with *Prunus* viruses A, B, and H, and with the viruses of rose and apple mosaics. It was not successful with some other viruses such as those of tobacco ringspot, cucumber mosaic, tomato spotted wilt, and peach yellow bud mosaic, all of which adsorbed to, and sedimented with, the calcium phosphate. By combining the use of phosphate with carborundum powder, the number of local lesions can be greatly increased. This is especially applicable to tobacco mosaic virus on the tobacco variety *xanthi-nc*. Fine carborundum powder is applied evenly to the leaves by sieving through fine mesh nylon taffeta; the virus, in a phosphate buffer, is then applied by means of a stiff brush (Takahashi, 1956). Similarly, Behara *et al.* (1956) obtained more local lesions with tobacco mosaic virus on Scotia bean (*Phaseolus vulgaris*) when the inoculum contained 10 per cent 600-mesh carborundum powder with 0·1M phosphate buffer at pH 8·5 as compared with simple inoculation.

*Treatment of Plants before and after Inoculation*

A most important environmental factor in the successful transmission of plant viruses by inoculation is the intensity of the light. Thus, reducing light intensity under which plants are grown in summer increased their susceptibility to infection with four viruses. With tobacco necrosis and tomato bushy stunt viruses, shading of the plants before inoculation increased the average number of local lesions per leaf by more than 10 times, and with the viruses of tobacco mosaic and aucuba mosaic by more than 5 times. Not only is susceptibility to infection enhanced but the actual virus content of the infected plant is also greatly increased. In the case of a strain of tobacco necrosis, the virus content was as much as 20 times greater than that of the controls. Since tobacco necrosis virus does not become systemic in tobacco, the plants referred to here, the increase in virus content applies only to the inoculated leaves. However, increases of up to 10 times in plants systemically infected with tomato bushy stunt virus were also obtained.

Furthermore, in the case of tobacco necrosis virus, there was the additional advantage that the total solid content of the sap was reduced by one-half. This, of course, greatly facilitates the purification of the virus (Bawden and Roberts, 1947). It should therefore be remembered when plants are being raised for virus purification or local lesion work that light intensity is of great importance.

Keeping the plants in complete darkness before and after sap-inoculation with tobacco mosaic virus results in a greater number of lesions on the leaves of *Nicotiana glutinosa* than on those kept in the light (Weintraub and Kemp, 1958). Not all plants of the same species react to a given virus with the same degree of susceptibility under pre-inoculation darkening, and one particular variety of tobacco may show a greater increase in susceptibility than others (Troutman and Fulton, 1958).

On the whole it seems to be the pre-inoculation shading or darkening which consistently increases the virus susceptibility of the test plants. Short periods in the dark seem to be equivalent to longer periods in the shade, but it must be remembered that different plant species react differently. The optimum conditions for bean plants (*Phaseolus vulgaris*) seem to be 24 hours in the dark before inoculation, whereas with tobacco plants susceptibility increases with increasing time in the dark up to 5 days (Bawden and Roberts, 1948).

The work of Kassanis (1952) and others suggests strongly that exposing the experimental plants to high temperatures before inoculation greatly increases susceptibility to many viruses, although it is clear that there is great variation in the reaction of different plants to different viruses under these conditions.

Keeping the test plants at 36°C for some time before inoculation has been shown by Kassanis greatly to increase their susceptibility to five sap-transmissible viruses, those of tomato wilt, tobacco mosaic, tobacco necrosis, tomato bushy stunt, and cucumber mosaic. The effects of post-inoculation treatment, however, differed with the various viruses according to whether they have high- or low-temperature coefficients of thermal inactivation. The viruses of tomato spotted wilt and tobacco mosaic can multiply in plants at 36°C, and post-inoculation treatment reduced the number of local lesions formed to between 10 and 90 per cent of the control. On the other hand, the viruses of tobacco necrosis, tomato bushy stunt, and cucumber mosaic, which do not multiply in the plant at 36°C, failed to form any local lesions at all when the plants were given post-inoculation heating.

If, as seems probable, it is the physiological condition of the plant which is affected by the high temperatures, then one would expect to get varying results according to the type of plant used. Plants of bean, *Phaseolus vulgaris*, become more resistant to infection with the virus of lucerne (alfalfa) mosaic if exposed either to low or to high temperatures before inoculation. The resistance imposed by temperatures is readily lost by the plants (Panzer, 1958).

Yarwood (1952) has shown that the susceptibility of test plants to virus infection can be greatly increased by applying the pre-inoculation heat to the plants in a different way. He actually immersed the plants in hot water for periods. When primary leaves of bean were heated 3 to 24 hours following inoculation, the number and size of local lesions resulting from inoculation with tobacco mosaic virus or with apple mosaic virus were increased as much as 20 times in comparison with unheated leaves. When bean leaves, var. Pinto, were heated by dipping in water at 50°C for 25 seconds, 6 hours after inoculation, the greatest increase in numbers of lesions resulted. Post-inoculation heating, however, was less effective than pre-inoculation heating for increasing the number of tobacco mosaic virus lesions. Post-inoculation heating of beans inoculated with lucerne mosaic virus delayed the appearance of local lesions, but when they did appear they were larger and more numerous than on the unheated leaves. Heating cucumber plants, which had passed the age of greatest susceptibility, for about 20 seconds at 50°C as late as 5 days after inoculation with the viruses of lucerne mosaic, apple mosaic, tomato spotted wilt, and peach yellow bud mosaic increased the number of systemically infected plants.

A certain amount of virus dissemination may take place by mechanical means which are not strictly inoculation. Some viruses, such as potato virus X, which are in high concentration in the plant can spread from a diseased plant to a healthy one by contact of the leaves brought about by the wind. Cultivation procedures and the movement of animals may play some part in the spread of viruses. According to Todd (1958), potato virus X can persist for as long as 6 weeks on the clothing of potato inspectors and of those who cultivate or spray the crop. Dogs and rabbits may also carry the virus on their feet and limbs. Tobacco mosaic virus is easily spread by means of contaminated hands or instruments and the tulip break virus is sometimes carried on the knife used to cut blooms, but this does not occur with the virus of narcissus stripe (van Slogteren and Ouboter, 1941). Similarly, the virus of cymbidium mosaic is readily spread by pruning shears (Jensen and Gold, 1955). Potato virus X may also be spread among potatoes in sacks by contact of the sprouts (Bawden, Kassanis, and Roberts, 1948). Some viruses may spread below ground by mechanical contact between the roots of infected and healthy plants. This was demonstrated by Roberts (1948, 1950) with potato virus X in potatoes and tomatoes, the spread being much more rapid by the roots of the tomato plants.

## Grafting

All viruses which are systemic in their hosts can be transmitted by grafting between susceptible and compatible plants. There are many methods of making grafts but only a few, which are suitable for use with herbaceous plants, are given here.

In the method of *detached scion grafting*, the wedge or cleft graft is commonly used; a small shoot is trimmed to a wedge and inserted in the cut stem of the stock. This cut should be made through a node if possible, otherwise the stem may be hollow. The scion should have most of its leaves removed and it should be inserted in the cleft of the stock so that the apical portions of the cut surfaces of the scion are just visible. The graft is then bound with bast, or preferably thin rubber tape, and

H

sealed with a drop of bicycle-tyre solution. The plant should then be placed in a moist atmosphere for a few days; it is not necessary to remove the rubber tape, since by the time a graft union is formed the rubber tape will have perished and fallen away.

This method is very suitable for studying the virus diseases of the tomato, potato, and tobacco plants, and it is usual for the scion to be virus-infected rather than the stock.

The other method of grafting suitable for herbaceous plants is known as *approach grafting*. In this type, the plants to be joined are brought together, but each retains parts above and below the point of contact. The simplest application of this method is known as the spliced approach graft. The stock and scion are each sliced to expose the cabium; the cut surfaces are then brought together and tied. The tongued approach graft is a suitable one for studying virus transmission and has been used by Harris (1932) and by Harris and King (1942) for investigating the virus diseases of strawberries. A 'tongue' is cut downwards on the stock and upwards on the scion; the tongues are then fitted together and wrapped with self-sealing crepe rubber.

Another method is known as *cleft inarching*; an upward cut in the stock forms the cleft and the scion is cut to a wedge to fit into the cleft. The whole must then be firmly tied.

A useful method is the bottle graft; here the leafy scion is approach-grafted to the stock, but the base of the scion is kept alive by immersion in a bottle of water until union is established, the base of the scion is then cut off close to the stock.

Modifications in grafting methods for studying the virus diseases of strawberries have been made by Bringhurst and Voth (1956). They cleft-grafted excised terminal leaflets from test plants to the petioles of indicator plants (*Fragaria vesca*). The scion leaflet is reduced by two-thirds, and the petiole, trimmed to a wedge, is inserted in a split in the stock petiole between the laterals, the terminal leaflet having been removed. Successful graft unions are quickly detected and the symptoms of virus disease develop within 2 to 5 weeks in *F. vesca*. Leaves can be grafted immediately after collecting in the field or stored in polythene bags for a month or more at 36°F before grafting.

Miller (1958) has studied the comparative efficiency of excised leaf-petiole grafts and stolon grafts for transmitting certain strawberry viruses. It was found that a prepared scion inserted in a slit made in the stock petiole, just below the lateral leaflets, without removing the terminal one, was as efficient as stolon grafting (approach method) in transmitting the strawberry mottle, vein-banding, latent and mild crinkle virus components to *Fragaria vesca* × *F. vesca* var. *alpina* indicator plants. Symptoms usually appeared 5 to 10 days earlier and were more severe.

Tuber-grafting is sometimes useful for the transmission of certain potato viruses. Cork borers of different sizes are used for this purpose; a core containing an eye is removed from the infected tuber and placed in the socket made in a healthy tuber by removing a plug with a cork borer one size smaller.

Tulip viruses can occasionally be transmitted by binding together infected and healthy halves of tulip bulbs.

For a comprehensive account of most known methods of grafting, the reader is referred to Garner (1958).

When it is desired to transmit a virus from a host which is unsuitable for study to one more suitable such as a herbaceous plant, a form of grafting using one or more species of the dodder, *Cuscuta* spp., is especially useful. By this means, grafting can be achieved between plants quite incompatible for ordinary grafting.

Schmelzer (1956) carried out experiments to determine the suitability of nine species of dodder as virus carriers. *Cuscuta campestris*, *C. californica*, *C. subinclusa*, *C. europaea*, and *C. epithymum* were almost uniformly effective in the transmission of the ordinary green strain of cucumber mosaic virus to *Nicotiana glutinosa*, but only 6 out of 40 tests with *C. lupuliformis* gave positive results.

Lucerne (alfalfa) mosaic virus was transmitted to tobacco var. *Samsun* by *C. campestris*, *C. subinclusa* (red and white leaved); *C. europaea* and *C. epilinum* did not act as carriers either in this test or in tests with potato stem-mottle. *C. campestris*, *C. gronovii*, and *C. lupuliformis* were the most effective carriers of potato stem-mottle virus to tobacco, while tobacco etch virus was transmitted to tobacco only by *C. lupuliformis*.

All the species of dodder gave negative results with bean yellow-mosaic virus, potato virus Y, and tomato black-ring virus (potato bouquet virus). Tomato spotted wilt virus was transmitted fairly well by *C. californica* to *N. glutinosa*, and tobacco mosaic virus to tobacco by *C. campestris*.

The virus of chrysanthemum flower distortion can be transmitted by *C. campestris* to periwinkle, *Vinca rosea* (Brierley and Smith, 1957).

## Vegetative Propagation

If a plant is virus-infected, all the vegetative parts used to propagate it will contain the virus, so that new plants produced by this method will also be virus-infected. It is for this reason that virus diseases are of such paramount importance in the potato crop, in raspberry and strawberry culture, in the bulb industry, and in many other crops which are produced from vegetative parts.

Much damage to fruit trees and roses arises from the use of root stocks or scions which may carry a latent virus infection. A classic case is the loss of many million orange trees with the Tristeza disease, or 'decline', of sweet oranges (Fawcett and Wallace, 1946). Sweet oranges grafted on to a sour orange root stock wilted and died of an apparent root rot. It was ascertained, however, that the sweet orange scion 'carried' a virus to which the sour orange stock was intolerant, so that when the root stock was killed the sweet orange grafted on to it died also. However, if the sweet orange scion was removed and established as a cutting, it survived and grew, because it was tolerant of the virus it carried whereas the sour orange was not.

There may be a few exceptions to the rule that all the vegetative parts of a virus-infected plant contain virus. Where the virus is not completely systemic in the host, it is sometimes possible to obtain virus-free cuttings; this applies particularly to the meristematic tissue (see Chapter Fourteen). If potato tubers are harvested while still immature from a plant recently infected, the virus may not have reached all the tubers. In potato plants infected with the virus of tomato spotted wilt, a percentage of the tubers seems to be virus-free.

## Seed Transmission

There is scope for considerable investigation into the phenomenon of seed transmission of viruses, since knowledge of this subject is very meagre. Crowley (1957) states that of the several hundred plant viruses described (actually more than 300) only 45 are known to be seed-transmitted and in only 4 of these does the transmission exceed 50 per cent.

Tobacco ringspot and tomato ringspot viruses show a high percentage of seed transmission in early infections (Kahn, 1956; Desjardins *et al.*, 1954), and Athow and Bancroft (1959) report 100 per cent seed transmission of tobacco ringspot virus in soybean.

In lettuce mosaic, the proportion of infected seed may vary considerably; in one variety of lettuce the percentage of seeds infected with mosaic virus varied from 0·2 to 14·2. Plants infected just before flowering produce fewer infected plants than those infected when young, and plants infected after flowering produce none. In some lettuce varieties the virus is not seed-transmitted at all, and this is governed by the particular response of the plant to infection. An example of this is given by the variety Cheshunt Early Giant, because the first formed floral heads are killed by infection and any secondary shoots formed contain little virus. The lettuce mosaic virus is also passed through the seed of groundsel, *Senecio vulgaris* L., which rarely shows symptoms but from which the virus may be transmitted by aphids to lettuce (Broadbent, 1958).

Some interesting studies on the seed-transmission of the virus causing false stripe disease of barley have been carried out. Rod-shaped particles measuring 30 mμ by 130 mμ have been found by electron microscopy to be associated with the disease. These particles occur in large numbers, and are found in the leaves, embryos, endosperm, pollen, and unfertilized pistils. Pollen transmission of the disease was suggested by the presence of the rods in seed produced from healthy pistils pollinated by pollen from diseased plants. Seed from diseased pollen and healthy pistils produced a small percentage of diseased seedlings (Gold, Suneson, Houston, and Oswald, 1954).

Transmission of a virus through the seed of one host species but not through the seed of another also occurs. There are several examples of this; the virus of cucumber mosaic is transmitted through the seed of the wild cucumber (*Micrampelis lobata*) but not apparently through the seed of the cultivated cucumber (Doolittle and Walker, 1925). Mahoney (1935) offers evidence that the virus is also carried in the seed of certain inbred lines of muskmelon, *Cucumis melo* L.

The virus of cowpea mosaic is transmitted by the seed of the asparagus bean, a variety of *Vigna unguiculata*, but not by the seed of the cow-pea (*Vigna sinensis*). Similarly, the tobacco ringspot virus is not carried in the seed of the tobacco plant but is present in the seed of *Petunia* sp. (Henderson, 1931) and of the Lincoln variety of soybean (Desjardins, Latterell, and Mitchell, 1954).

Other examples are the transmission of *Abutilon* mosaic virus through the seed of certain species only (Keur, 1933), and of the dodder latent mosaic virus through the seed of *Cuscuta campestris* but not through the seed of cantaloupe, buckwheat, and pokeweed, *Phytolacca americana* L. (Bennett, 1944), and of tomato ringspot virus through the seed of the Lincoln variety of soybean (Kahn, 1956). Cadman (1963) points out that all the nematode-transmitted viruses are apparently seed-borne.

A study has been recently published on the seed transmission of nematode-borne viruses which gives more detailed information (Lister and Murant, 1967). Seed transmission occurred with tomato black-ring virus (TBRV) in 19 species (13 botanical families), with *Arabis* mosaic virus (AMV) in 13 species (11 families), with raspberry ringspot virus (RRV) in 6 species (5 families), and also with tomato ringspot, cherry leaf-roll, and tobacco rattle viruses. Most of the seedlings except those containing tobacco rattle virus appeared to be symptomless carriers. The occurrence and extent of seed transmission depended on both virus and host plant; in many progenies more than 10 per cent, and in some 100 per cent, of seedlings were infected. The viruses were transmitted through at least 2 or 3 generations of seed of these host species tested.

After 6 years' storage, seed from *Capsella bursapastoris* and *Stellaria media* infected with tomato blackring virus and raspberry ringspot virus gave rise to infected seedlings.

For information on seed transmission in the ecology of nematode-borne viruses see Murant and Lister (1967).

As a rule, seed-transmitted viruses are carried internally, and treating the seed so as to inactivate any virus adhering to the external seed coat does not reduce appreciably the percentage of seed transmission (Athow and Bancroft, 1959). Long storage results in a gradual loss of virus in the seed; it has been shown that there is a marked decrease in the percentage of seed transmission of musk melon mosaic virus after 3 years (Rader *et al.*, 1947).

There has for long been a controversy as to whether or not the virus of tobacco mosaic (tomato strain) is carried in the seed of tomatoes; this is a matter of considerable importance to glasshouse growers of tomatoes. Chamberlain and Fry (1950) and Taylor *et al.* (1961) found that most of the TMV present with tomato seed is in or on the seed coat.

Broadbent (1965) has made an intensive study of the whole question and the following account is from his work. In a given tomato strain of TMV the cleaned seeds from infected fruits average about 50 per cent infection. In most cases the virus was carried externally, but a percentage of seed carried it within the testa or the endosperm. High virus concentrations sometimes occurred internally, usually when the endosperm was infected. Endosperm infection occurred mainly in fruits from flowers that set after the plants were infected. The presence of virus within the embryo was never confirmed.

Treating the fruit-pulp with one quarter of its volume of concentrated hydrochloric acid for 30 minutes was the best method of cleaning seeds and of eliminating any virus on the seed coat.

The only treatment that often eliminated TMV carried internally was to heat dry seeds in an oven at 70°C; treatment for 3 days was usually enough to free seeds completely but much longer treatment failed to eliminate virus from the endosperm.

TMV was lost after a few months' storage with some stocks of seed, but persisted for as long as 9 years in others with endosperm infection.

In 1964, infection of apple trees with TMV was shown by Kirkpatrick and Lindner, and, interestingly enough, seed transmission of this virus was demonstrated in young direct-seeded seedlings of apple, pear, and *Malus platycarpa* (Gilmer and Wilks, 1967).

The reason for the rarity of seed transmission of viruses in general is not known, but Bennett (1940) suggested that they are unable to maintain themselves in gametophytic tissue, a view supported by Crowley (1957).

### References

ATHOW, K. L. and BANCROFT, J. B. (1959) *Phytopathology.* **49**, 697.

AINSWORTH, G. C. (1936) *Nature.* **137**, 868.

BALD, J. G. and SAMUEL, G. (1934) *Ann. appl. Biol.* **21**, 179–90.

BAWDEN, F. C. (1950) *Plant Viruses and Virus Diseases.* 3rd ed. Waltham, Mass: Chronica Botanica Co.

BAWDEN, F. C., KASSANIS, B., and ROBERTS, F. M. (1948) *Ann. appl. Biol.* **35**, 250–65.

BAWDEN, F. C. and ROBERTS, F. M. (1947) *Ann. appl. Biol.* **34**, 286–96.

BAWDEN, F. C. and ROBERTS, F. M. (1948) *Ann. appl. Biol.* **35**, 418–28.

BEHARA, L., VARZANDEH, M., and THORNBERRY, H. H. (1956) *Virology.* **1**, 141–51.

BENNETT, C. W. (1940) *Bot. Review.* **6**, 427.

BENNETT, C. W. (1944) *Phytopathology.* **34**, 77–91.

BRIERLEY, P. and SMITH, F. F. (1957) *Phytopathology.* **47**, 448–50.

BRINGHURST, R. S. and VOTH, M. (1956) *Plant Dis. Reptr.* **40**, 596–600.

BROADBENT, L. (1958) *Sci. Hort.* **13**, 74–9.

BROADBENT, L. (1965) *Ann. appl. Biol.* **56**, 177–205.

CADMAN, C. H. (1963) *Ann. Rev. Phytopathol.* **1**, 143–72.

CHAMBERLAIN, E. E. and FRY, P. R. (1950) *New Zealand J. Sci. Technol.* (*A*) **32**, 19.

CHESTER, K. S. (1935) *Science.* **82**, 17.

CROWLEY, N. C. (1957) *Australian J. Biol. Sci.* **10**, 449.

DALE, J. L. (1956) *Diss. Abstr.* **16**, 1566.

DESJARDINS, P. R., LATTERELL, R. J., and MITCHELL, J. E. (1954) *Phytopathology.* **44**, 86.

DOOLITTLE, S. P. and WALKER, M. N. (1925) *J. Agric. Res.* **31**, 1–58.

FAWCETT, H. S. and WALLACE, S. M. (1946) *Calif. Citrogr.* **32**, 50.

FULTON, R. W. (1957) *Phytopathology,* **47**, 512.

GARNER, R. J. (1958) *The Grafter's Handbook.* pp. 1–260. London: Faber and Faber.

GILMER, R. M. and WILKS, J. M. (1967) *Phytopathology.* **57**, 214–17.

GOLD, A. H., SUNESON, C. A., HOUSTON, B. R., and OSWALD, J. W. (1954) *Phytopathology.* **44**, 115.

HARRIS, R. V. (1932) *J. Pomol.* **10**, 35–41.

HARRIS, R. V. and KING, M. E. (1942) *J. Pomol.* **19**, 227–42.

HENDERSON, R. G. (1931) *Phytopathology.* **21**, 225–9.

HOLMES, F. O. (1929) *Bot. Gaz.* **87**, 39–55.

HOLMES, F. O. (1952) *Indian Phytopathology.* **5**, 9–10.

JENSEN, D. D. and GOLD, A. H. (1955) *Phytopathology.* **45**, 327–34.

KAHN, R. P. (1956) *Phytopathology.* **46**, 295.

KASSANIS, B. (1952) *Ann. appl. Biol.* **39**, 358–68.

KEUR, J. Y. (1933) *Phytopathology.* (Abstr.) **23**, 20.

KIRKPATRICK, H. C. and LINDNER, R. C. (1964) *Plant Dis. Reptr.* **48**, 855–7.

KUNKEL, L. O. (1934) *Phytopathology.* **24**, 437–66.

LAUFFER, M. and PRICE, W. C. (1945) *Arch. Biochem.* **8**, 449–68.

LINDNER, R. C. and KIRKPATRICK, H. C. (1959) *Phytopathology.* **49**, 78.

LISTER, R. M. and MURANT, A. F. (1967) *Ann. appl. Biol.* **59**, 49–62.

MAHONEY, C. H. (1935) *Proc. Amer. Soc. Hort. Sci.* **32**, 477–80.

MCKINNEY, H. H. and FELLOWES, H. (1951) *Plant Dis. Reptr.* **35**, 264–6.

MILLER, P. W. (1958) *Plant Dis. Reptr.* **42**, 1043–7.

MURANT, A. F. and LISTER, R. M. (1967) *Ann. appl. Biol.* **59**, 63–76.

PANZER, J. D. (1958) *Phytopathology.* **48**, 550–2.

RADER, W. E., FITZPATRICK, H. F., and HILDEBRAND, E. M. (1947) *Phytopathology.* **37**, 809.

RAWLINS, T. E. and TOMPKINS, C. M. (1936) *Phytopathology.* **26**, 578–87.

ROBERTS, F. M. (1948) *Ann. appl. Biol.* **25**, 266–78.

ROBERTS, F. M. (1950) *Ann. appl. Biol.* **37**, 385–96.

SAMUEL, G. (1931) *Ann. appl. Biol.* **18**, 494–507.

SCHMELZER, K. (1956) *Phytopathol. Z.* **28**, 1–56.

SLOGTEREN, VAN, E. and OUBOTER, M. P. DE B. (1941) *Meded. Landbouwhoogeschool, Wageningen.* **45**, 32 pp.

STEERE, R. (1955) *Phytopathology.* **45**, 196–208.

TAKAHASHI, W. N. (1947) *Amer. J. Bot.* **34**, 496–500.

TAKAHASHI, W. N. (1956) *Phytopathology.* **46**, 654–6.

TAYLOR, R. H., GROGAN, R. G., and KIMBLE, K. A. (1961) *Phytopathology,* **51**, 837.

TODD, J. M. (1958) *Proc. 3rd Conf. Pot. Virus Dis.* 1951. Wageningen-Lisse. pp. 71–5. N. Holland Publ. Co.

TROUTMAN, J. L. and FULTON, R. W. (1958) *Virology.* **6**, 303–16.

WEINTRAUB, M. and KEMP, W. G. (1958) *Canad. J. Bot.* **36**, 455–6.

YARWOOD, C. E. (1952) *Phytopathology.* **42**, 654–6.

YARWOOD, C. E. (1953) *Plant Dis. Reptr.* **37**, 501–2.

YARWOOD, C. E. (1955) *Virology,* **I**, 268–85.

YARWOOD, C. E. (1957) *Adv. Vir. Res.* **4**, 249.

YARWOOD, C. E. (1957a) *Phytopathology.* **47**, 613–14.

# CHAPTER TEN

# Quantitative Assay. Virus Inhibitors. Virus Strains

## Quantitative Assay

There are two main methods for making a quantitative assay of plant viruses. One is the serological method, which is dealt with in Chapter Eleven. The other is the 'local lesion' method, the outline of which is given here.

Certain host plants react to certain viruses in such a way that the virus is localized on the inoculated leaf in discrete necrotic spots, the local lesions (Plate 14). This localization may be permanent, as in the case of tobacco mosaic virus on the leaves of *Nicotiana glutinosa*, or there may be a coalescence of the points of infection, as with tobacco necrosis virus (TNV) on the leaves of bean (*Phaseolus vulgaris*), or systemic infection of the plant may follow, as in the case of potato virus X (PVX) on the tobacco plant. The latter is no longer used as a local lesion host for PVX, its place being taken by *Gomphrena globosa* which reacts with permanent discrete lesions.

Where there is no systemic spread of the virus, the use of local lesions allows the recognition of large numbers of successful transmissions on single plants. In 1929, Holmes, using TMV, showed that the number of lesions varied with the virus content of the inoculum; leaves rubbed with undiluted sap produced hundreds of lesions while leaves rubbed with a 1:1,000 dilution produced only a few. This allows for comparative estimates of virus concentrations. At higher concentrations of the virus there is no direct and simple relationship between the concentration and the numbers of lesions produced, but within certain limits it is possible to tell which of two samples of virus is the more concentrated, and to gain some idea of their relative virus content. It would be quite wrong, however, as Bawden (1964) has emphasized, to translate differences in numbers of lesions directly to differences of virus content. Nevertheless, in a properly designed experiment, results of a considerable degree of accuracy can be obtained.

There are many variables to be taken into account when using the local lesion method and much work has been carried out to try to make the results statistically correct. It is important that the plants to be used should be of comparable age, size, and colour, and all should have the same nutritional treatment. In using *N. glutinosa*, for example, the number of leaves should be reduced to four or five and the growing point removed.

One of the variables mentioned above is the fact that all the leaves of the same plant do not react to inoculation in the same manner. It was shown by Samuel and Bald (1933), however, that there was little difference between the reaction of opposite halves of the same leaves, and that, by comparing preparations on opposite half-leaves, fewer plants were necessary and more accurate results obtained. Bawden (1950) points out that the simplest way is to select one preparation as a standard and apply it to one-half of every leaf, while the other half-leaves are apportioned between the other preparations. Each preparation can then be compared directly with the standard and indirectly through the standard with any other.

Youden and Beale (1934) used the Latin square to permit the intercomparison of a number of virus preparations without unnecessary duplication of a reference standard. This is accomplished by so distributing the several treatments among the leaves that each appears equally often on each plant and each leaf position. Thus, if five virus preparations are to be compared, using five plants each having five leaves, each virus preparation is inoculated on to a total of five leaves, once on each plant and once in each leaf position.

Steere (1955) suggests that one should designate a right and a left side, and inoculate the right sides of half the leaves with one preparation and the left halves of the same leaves with the second preparation. The right halves of the remaining leaves should then be inoculated with the second preparation and the left halves with the first. This will provide a balance against unequal manipulation of the two halves of a leaf.

For information on the statistical aspects of the local lesion technique, the reader is referred to Kleczkowski (1949, 1950, 1955), Fry and Taylor (1954), and Roberts (1964).

The number of local lesions is increased if an abrasive, celite or carborundum powder, is added to the inoculum. Great care, however, must be used or the leaf will be damaged; it is important, also, to inoculate each leaf as uniformly as possible, so that one does not receive greater pressure than another. Each half leaf should be washed immediately after inoculation to remove any excess inoculum which might injure the leaf if allowed to dry. The washing, however, should be brief and should not be longer than 2 to 3 seconds.

The local-lesion host must also be chosen with care. For tobacco mosaic virus, the favourite plant in the U.S.A. is one or more varieties of bean (*P. vulgaris*), such as Early Golden Cluster, Pinto, and others. In England, less success has been obtained with the bean varieties available; Canadian Wonder, for example, usually gives no local lesions with TMV. *N. glutinosa* is much used also for this virus, but its place is being taken by a variety of tobacco *xanthi* which has had the local lesion response bred into it and so acts in the same way as *N. glutinosa*.

For tobacco necrosis viruses, the bean is a suitable local lesion host, such as the varieties Canadian Wonder, Bountiful, and others. It should be remembered, however, that, unlike the lesions of tobacco mosaic virus, those of tobacco necrosis viruses on bean do not remain discrete but tend to coalesce if left for a few days. The lesions should therefore be counted immediately after they are fully developed. For cucumber mosaic virus, the bean is also a useful local lesion host, though some workers prefer the cowpea (*Vigna sinensis* Endl. var. Black) (Tomlinson *et al.*, 1958).

More information on suitable test plants will be found in Chapter Thirteen.

## Virus Inhibitors

One of the puzzling phenomena which confronts the student during inoculation studies with sap-transmissible viruses is the non-transmissibility of such viruses from certain plant hosts. This is usually due to the presence in the sap of the virus-infected plant of a substance which prevents infection with the virus when rubbed on the leaves of a susceptible plant. Such a substance is known as an 'inhibitor'; these inhibitors are not present only in the sap of certain plants: a wide range of miscellaneous substances also have the same inhibitor effect. In this discussion, however, we are mainly concerned with the inhibitors which occur naturally in plant sap and with which the student will come in contact during the study of sap-transmissible viruses. For a more detailed account of inhibitors from other sources and for a review of the whole subject, the reader is referred to Bawden (1954).

The first suggestion of an inhibitor in plant sap occurs in the work of Allard (1914, 1918), who worked with a mosaic disease of pokeweed, *Phytolacca decandra*. He was able to transmit the virus by sap-inoculation from pokeweed to pokeweed but not to tobacco. Later, Doolittle and Walker (1925) transmitted the same virus from pokeweed to healthy cucumber plants by means of aphids and showed the virus to be that of cucumber mosaic. They, also, failed to infect cucumber plants by mechanical inoculation. In the same year, Duggar and Armstrong (1925) experimented with the sap of *Phytolacca* and found that, when added to sap containing tobacco mosaic virus, it prevented the infection of healthy tobacco plants. These workers tested a number of other plants for the presence of inhibitors and found that the sap of the thorn apple, *Datura stramonium*, was also somewhat inhibitory.

Grant (1934) made a series of tests for the presence of inhibitors in the sap different plant species and found that the juice from spinach, *Spinacia oleracea*, beet, *Beta vulgaris*, and Swiss chard, *B. vulgaris* var. *cicla*, all contained an inhibitory substance.

It was not, however, until much later that a serious attempt was made to isolate the inhibitor from pokeweed. Kassanis and Kleczkowski (1948), by means of precipitation with alcohol, followed by adsorption on kieselguhr and elution with 10 per cent sodium chloride, identified it as a glycoprotein containing 14 to 15 per cent of nitrogen and 8 to 12 per cent carbohydrate. It occurs in the sap of *Phytolacca esculenta* leaves at the rate of 100 mg/1.

Kuntz and Walker (1947) studied the inhibitory substances in spinach sap and decided that there were two inhibitors present, one of which inhibits infection of tobacco with the cabbage black-ringspot virus but does not affect the transmission to tobacco of tobacco mosaic virus. This one withstands boiling, exposure to alcohol, and diffuses through cellophane; the other is destroyed by heating at 70°C, by 95 per cent alcohol and by acid pH below 3 or alkaline pH above 9·5, and does not diffuse through cellophane. This latter inhibitor may be a protein similar to that from *Phytolacca*, as suggested by Bawden (1954).

Another aspect of the subject is the importance of the host species in determining the action of virus inhibitors. Gendron and Kassanis (1954) consider that the extent to which infection is inhibited by those substances depends on the species of plants to which inoculations are made and not on the identity of the virus. The inhibitors are largely ineffective in preventing infection of the species which contain them. For example, sap from *Datura tatula* inhibits infections when inoculations are made to bean, *Phaseolus vulgaris*, and to beet, but not when made to *D. tatula*; and sap from beet inhibits infection of beans and *D. tatula* but not of beet.

There is one anomalous case which may be an exception to this behaviour. It is extremely difficult to infect young plants of lovage (*Ligusticum scoticum*) with a mosaic virus from an infected lovage plant, although the virus is easily transmitted by sap-inoculation to tobacco and many other plant species (Smith and Markham, 1944).

A few examples of plants which contain inhibitors of virus infection follow: dahlia mosaic virus sap-transmissible from infected to healthy *Zinnia elegans*, but not from this species to dahlia (Brierley and Smith, 1950); carnation mosaic virus from carnation (*Dianthus caryophyllus*) to carnation, but rarely from carnation to bean or tobacco (van der Want, 1951); tobacco ringspot virus easily transmissible from infected to healthy sweet william (*Dianthus barbatus*), but not from sweet william to tobacco or cucumber (Weintraub and Gilpatrick, 1952).

In experiments at Cambridge with a virus from *Ranunculus* sp. in New Zealand spinach (*Tetragonia expansa*), it was found easy to transmit the virus from and to New Zealand spinach but not from that plant to other susceptible plant species. Benda (1956) finds that expressed sap of New Zealand spinach when mixed with tobacco ringspot virus inoculated by rubbing on to cowpea (*Vigna sinensis*) leaves caused a delay in the appearance of the primary virus symptoms. The spinach sap appeared to contain two active fractions, one an inhibitor which decreased the number of lesions but was destroyed by heat, and the other an augmenter, identified indirectly as a soluble oxalate salt, which increased the number of lesions. The writer has found that the virus of western ringspot gives very clear local lesions in the form of concentric rings on the inoculated leaves of *Chenopodium amaranticolor* but is not sap-transmissible from this to other plants.

Healthy and infected cucumber-plant extracts have been found highly inhibitory to cucumber mosaic virus. The inhibitor is present in almost all parts of the cucumber plant with the exception of the corollas. It has been detected in green leaves, dead leaves, cotyledons, stems, etiolated seedlings, roots, seeds, fruits, and entire blossoms (Sill and Walker, 1952).

An inhibitor from rice leaves, which is also present in the flowers, roots, kernels, culms, polish from the rice, and in heat-dried and frozen leaves, prevents the infection of leaves of pinto bean (*Phaseolus vulgaris*) with tobacco mosaic virus (Allen and Kahn, 1957).

In the expressed sap of various species of dodder (*Cuscuta* spp.) are substances inhibitory to the development of the following viruses: tomato spotted wilt virus on *Nicotiana glutinosa*; lucerne (alfalfa) mosaic virus on *Phaseolus vulgaris*; cabbage black-ringspot virus on tobacco; potato virus Y on *Physalis floridana*, potato virus X on tobacco and *Amaranthus retroflexus*; cucumber mosaic virus on cowpea (*Vigna sinensis*); potato rattle virus on *N. glutinosa*; and tomato bushy stunt virus on *N. glutinosa* (Schmelzer, 1956).

Bawden and Pirie (1957) have isolated a virus-inactivating system even from the leaves of the tobacco plant, probably the most virus-susceptible of all plants. The exposure of stable virus preparations of the Rothamsted strain of tobacco necrosis virus to leaf-sap sediment, which had been centrifuged at 4,000 to 8,000$g$, in the presence of air, inactivated them. This accounts for the variations in infectivity in tobacco necrosis viruses prepared from tobacco sap by different methods.

Inhibitors of another type occur in a number of plant species; these are tannins and they are probably the reason for the difficulty in transmitting mechanically the viruses occurring in rosaceous plants, particularly strawberries and raspberries. When leaves, stems, or roots of strawberry plants are macerated, extracted with a little water, and the extracts centrifuged, the supernatant fluid contains no protein. Enough tannin is liberated to precipitate all the plant protein and the supernatant still contains enough tannin to precipitate tobacco mosaic virus and prevent it from infecting *N. glutinosa* (Bawden and Kleczkowski, 1945). Thresh

(1956) suggests methods for increasing the efficiency of virus extraction by preventing or reversing the precipitation of proteins which normally occurs on macerating tissues containing tannins. Since tannins are not uniformly distributed throughout the plant, and their concentration varies with the season, it is evident that the best inoculation results will be obtained by selecting tissues with a high virus content and the minimum amount of tannin. In the undamaged cell, tannins are localized in the vacuole and separated from the protoplast, so that the simplest way to avoid virus precipitation is to complete the inoculation before the tannins have had time to accumulate and combine with the proteins released when the leaves are macerated. A quick method of inoculation such as Yarwood's leaf-disc method (see Chapter Nine) is therefore to be recommended where tannins are present.

In cases where the virus is precipitated by the tannins of the host, it may be possible to recover infective virus by centrifuging the expressed sap. Thresh (*loc. cit.*) suggests that this may be the explanation of Bennett's (1955) recovery of infective curly-top preparations from the precipitate which forms rapidly in expressed sap of the water pimpernel (*Samolus parviflorus* Raf.).

Limasset (1951) found that nicotine sulphate increased the infectivity of saps containing tannins, and Thresh showed that tannic acid in the inoculum inhibited less in the presence of nicotine sulphate. Cadman (1956) used the same substance in experiments with raspberry viruses. In extracting the virus from raspberry leaves, 40 ml of 40 per cent nicotine sulphate solution was applied per 30 g of leaf tissue. Later (Cadman, 1959), he found nicotine base more effective than the sulphate. He also tried removing tannins by adsorption and found that alumina was effective in removing inhibitors from raspberry and strawberry leaf extracts.

## Virus Strains

Very few plant viruses, particularly those of the sap-transmissible mosaic type, are single entities but consist of several strains. This is well illustrated by tobacco mosaic virus; frequently one or more 'yellow' variants show up on a mottled leaf as yellow spots of varying sizes.

It has long been known that after passage of particular plant hosts some viruses appear to have undergone a change which is expressed in increased or decreased virulence. A classical example of this is the apparent reduction in virulence of the beet curly-top virus after passage through *Chenopodium murale* (Carsner and Stahl, 1924), and its apparent reactivation after passage of *Stellaria media* (Lackey, 1932). However, the most probable explanation is not that the virus has undergone any change but that the particular host plant favours the more rapid development of another strain of the virus already present in the inoculum, which thus obscures the virus strain which was dominant in the plant from which the inoculum was obtained. This is shown by two examples. Johnson (1947) inoculated the sea holly (*Eryngium aquaticum*) with virulent strains of tobacco mosaic virus and could always recover mild strains from the infected plant. Similarly, Matthews (1949) found that the tree tomato, *Cyphomandra betacea*, has the property of selecting out a severe strain when inoculated with potato virus X.

It will be well to bear in mind, however, that apparent alterations to viruses by passage of certain hosts do occur. Bawden (1958) has shown that a particular strain of tobacco mosaic virus mutates on passage between beans (*Phaseolus vulgaris*) and tobacco, and Watson (1956) considers that potato virus C alters its insect-vector relationship after passage of Majestic potato.

A practical method of isolating virus strains is by sub-inoculation from the spontaneously developing yellow spots in mottled leaves, previously mentioned, or from local lesions. There is a good deal of evidence which suggests that only one virus particle is concerned in the production of a local lesion. That being so, sub-inoculation of individual local lesions to plants in which the virus becomes systemic is a convenient method for isolating virus strains. To obtain the lesion inoculum, it is necessary to use a local lesion host in which the lesions remain discrete and do not coalesce. *Nicotiana glutinosa* and some varieties of bean (*Phaseolus vulgaris*) are suitable for tobacco mosaic virus, while some of the chenopodiaceous indicator plants such as *Gomphrena globosa* and *Chenopodium amaranticolor* can be used for other viruses (see Chapter Thirteen). Using the local lesion method, Jensen (1933, 1936, 1937) isolated over fifty strains of tobacco mosaic virus; some of his strains are similar to those found in nature. Others, however, by their lack of ability to spread in the tobacco plant would not survive in the field.

Price (1934) obtained a number of variants of cucumber mosaic virus

I

by cutting out yellow spots from mottled leaves, and one of these yellow variants is still unchanged after 30 years. By its unmistakable bright yellow mottling, it serves a useful purpose in cross-immunization tests with other suspected strains of cucumber mosaic virus. It seems therefore that viruses, particularly those that, like TMV, exist in high concentration in the plant, are continually mutating to give rise to new strains.

We have seen that plant virus strains differ in symptomatology and in virulence, but they also differ in other ways. It was pointed out in Chapter Eight that strains of viruses with their specific nematode vectors exist and Black (1944) has shown that there is a similar state of affairs with the leafhopper transmission of strains of potato yellow-dwarf virus. Furthermore, he has shown (Black, 1953) that certain leafhopper-borne viruses lose their affinity for their insect vectors and become vector-less strains. Changes in antigenic properties have been found (Aach 1957), and Knight (1947) and Knight et al. (1962) have shown, respectively, differences in amino acid composition and slight changes in nucleic acid structure of TMV strains.

As a rule, the morphology of a virus and its strains is the same, but according to Corbett (1967) the virus of *Odontoglossum* ringspot, a strain of TMV, has a particle 20 m$\mu$ longer than that of the type virus.

## References

AACH, H. G. (1957) Z. Naturforsch. 12b, 614.

ALLARD, H. A. (1914) U.S. Dept. Agric. Bull. No. 40.

ALLARD, H. A. (1918) Phytopathology. 8, 51–4.

ALLEN, T. C. and KAHN, R. P. (1957) Phytopathology. (Abstr). 47, 515.

BAWDEN, F. C. (1950) Plant Viruses and Virus Diseases. 3rd ed. Waltham, Mass: Chronica Botanica Co.

BAWDEN, F. C. (1954) Adv. Vir. Res. 2, 31–57.

BAWDEN, F. C. (1958) J. Gen. Microbiol. 18, 751–66.

BAWDEN, F. C. (1964) Plant Viruses and Virus Diseases. 4th ed. p. 157. New York: Ronald Press Co.

BAWDEN, F. C. and KLECZKOWSKI, A. (1945) J. Pomol. 21, 2–7.

BAWDEN, F. C. and PIRIE, N. W. (1957) J. Gen. Microbiol. 16, 696–710.

BENDA, G. T. A. (1956) Virology. 2, 438–54.

BENNETT, C. W. (1955) Phytopathology. 45, 531–6.

BLACK, L. M. (1944) Proc. Amer. Phil. Soc. 88, 132–44.

BLACK, L. M. (1953) Phytopathology. 43, 466.

BRIERLEY, P. and SMITH, F. F. (1950) Plant Dis. Reptr. 34, 363–70.

CADMAN, C. H. (1956) *J. hort. Sci.* **31**, 111–18.

CADMAN, C. H. (1959) *J. gen. Microbiol.* **20**, 113.

CARSNER, E. and STAHL, C. E. (1924) *Phytopathology.* (Abstr.) **14**, 57.

CORBETT, M. K. (1967) *Phytopathology.* **57**, 164–72.

DOOLITTLE, S. P. and WALKER, M. N. (1925) *J. agric. Res.* **31**, 1–55.

DUGGAR, B. M. and ARMSTRONG, J. K. (1925) *Ann. Missouri Bot. Garden.* **12**, 359–66.

FRY, P. R. and TAYLOR, W. B. (1954) *Ann. appl. Biol.* **41**, 664.

GENDRON, Y. and KASSANIS, B. (1954) *Ann. appl. Biol.* **41**, 183–8.

GRANT, T. J. (1934) *Phytopathology.* **24**, 331–6.

HOLMES, F. O. (1929) *Bot. Gaz.* **87**, 39–55.

JENSEN, J. H. (1933) *Phytopathology.* **23**, 964–74.

JENSEN, J. H. (1936) *Phytopathology.* **26**, 266–77.

JENSEN, J. H. (1937) *Phytopathology.* **27**, 69–84.

JOHNSON, J. (1947) *Phytopathology.* **37**, 822–37.

KASSANIS, B. and KLECZKOWSKI, A. (1948) *J. Gen. Microbiol.* **2**, 143–53.

KLECZKOWSKI, A. (1949) *Ann. appl. Biol.* **36**, 139.

KLECZKOWSKI, A. (1950) *J. Gen. Microbiol.* **4**, 53.

KLECZKOWSKI, A. (1955) *J. Gen. Microbiol.* **13**, 91.

KNIGHT, C. A. (1947) *J. Biol. Chem.* **171**, 297.

KNIGHT, C. A., SILVA, D. M., DAHL, D., and TSUGITA, A. (1962) *Virology.* **16**, 236.

KUNTZ, J. E. and WALKER, J. C. (1947) *Phytopathology.* **37**, 561–79.

LACKEY, C. F. (1932) *J. agric. Res.* **44**, 755–65.

LIMASSET, P. (1951) *Atti. Soc. Ital. Patol.* **2**, 911–17.

MATTHEWS, R. E. F. (1948) *Parasitology.* **39**, 241–4.

PRICE, W. C. (1934) *Phytopathology.* **24**, 743–61.

ROBERTS, D. A. (1964) in *Plant Virology*, pp. 194–210. Eds. M. K. Corbett and H. D. Sister, Gainesville: Univ. of Florida Press.

SAMUEL, G. and BALD, J. G. (1933) *Ann. appl. Biol.* **20**, 70–99.

SCHMELZER, K. (1956) *Zbl. Bakt. Abt. 2*, **109**, 20–2.

SILL, W. H. and WALKER, J. C. (1952) *Phytopathology.* **42**, 349–52.

SMITH, K. M. and MARKHAM, R. (1944) *Phytopathology.* **34**, 324–9.

STEERE, R. L. (1955) *Phytopathology.* **45**, 196–208.

THRESH, J. M. (1956) *Ann. appl. Biol.* **44**, 608–18.

TOMLINSON, J. A., SHEPHERD, R. J., and WALKER, J. C. (1958) *Nature.* **182**, 1616.

VAN DER WANT, J. P. H. (1951) *Tijdschr. PlZiekt.* **57**, 72–4.

WATSON, M. A. (1956) *Ann. appl. Biol.* **44**, 599–607.

WEINTRAUB, M. and GILPATRICK, J. D. (1952) *Canad. J. Bot.* **30**, 549–57.

YOUDEN, W. J. and BEALE, H. P. (1934) *Contr. Boyce Thompson Inst. Pl. Res.* **6**, 437–54.

# CHAPTER ELEVEN

# Serology of Plant Viruses

Before briefly describing the serology of plant viruses, it will be well to define some of the terms used. When an animal is infected with a pathogen, whether it be virus or bacterium, or injected with a *foreign* protein, there are produced, in the blood-stream, proteins which combine specifically with the substance injected. This act of combination can be demonstrated *in vitro* in several ways and forms the basis of serological tests. The proteins produced in response to the stimulus of the injected substance or pathogen are called *antibodies*, and they can be formed not only in response to disease agents but to many other foreign materials including of course normal plant proteins. This is important because it may lead to wrong conclusions about plant virus relationships.

Any substance which will stimulate the production of antibodies and which will combine with them *in vitro* is called an *antigen*. A serum containing antibodies is called an *antiserum*; while serum from an animal which has not been injected with any antigens is called *normal*.

To obtain the antiserum, the rabbit is the animal generally used, though the domestic fowl and also the horse have been employed. The injections are either intraperitoneal or intraveinal and the quantity of virus (antigen) used at each injection is about 5 ml.

Better results with less virus can be obtained if Freund's Adjuvant is added to the inoculum. This consists of a paraffin-base mineral oil mixed with a specific surface-active agent, mannide mono-oleate at a ratio of 9 parts to 1. Equal parts of the oil mixture and virus suspension are emulsified (Ball, 1964).

Since it was first shown, by Purdy Beale in 1928, that the sap from mosaic-diseased tobacco plants contains an antigen specific for virus-containing extracts and one not present in the sap of healthy tobacco plants, much research has been carried out on the antigenicity of plant viruses. Many other plant viruses are now known to be good antigens, especially those which are fairly stable and occur in high concentration in the plant sap. After the first discovery of Purdy Beale, it was shown by Gratia (1933 a and b) that plants containing different viruses contained also different specific antigens; while Birkeland (1934) showed that strains of plant viruses also contained specific antigens which differentiated them from other members of the group.

Four types of serological reaction have been used in plant virus work.

(1) *Neutralization* of the properties of the virus.

(2) *Complement Fixation Test.* When antigens are mixed with their specific antibodies, the mixture has the property of removing the power of normal serum to haemolyse sensitized red corpuscles. It is a kind of delicate colour indicator test. Complement is a heat-labile substance present in normal blood serum.

(3) *Precipitin Reaction.* A precipitate is formed when the virus is added to its specific antiserum in saline at different dilutions and warmed in a water-bath. In precipitation the antibody is referred to as *precipitin*.

(4) *Anaphylaxis.* In this test the union between antigen and antibody is detected by reactions in animal tissues.

We are only concerned here with the precipitin reaction and its application in plant virology, but for an excellent account of plant virus serology generally the reader is referred to a monograph by Matthews (1957). Another comprehensive and more recent review of the same subject has been written by van Regenmortel (1966).

## Preparation of the Viruses (Antigens)

Since we know that normal plant proteins are also antigens and that some of them, particularly those from solanaceous plants, are toxic to animals, preliminary clarification of the virus-containing sap is necessary. Removal of the plant proteins during clarification is not easy, since those methods which remove most of the proteins are liable greatly to reduce virus concentration. Freezing the leaves before mincing or grinding assists in the coagulation of plant material. With some viruses having a high thermal inactivation point, heating the expressed sap to 50 to 60°C for a few minutes will remove much toxic material; this is important when using solanaceous plants.

Van Regenmortel (1966) has pointed out how the presence of plant proteins in the inoculum may lead to wrong conclusions. It was shown by Moritz (1964) that a number of plants possess serologically related protein antigens, and there are many instances of serological cross-reactions between antigens present in the sap of healthy plants belonging to different species. Because of this, it is not possible to eliminate unwanted reactions with contaminating host antigens by propagating the virus in a different plant species from that used to obtain the antigen source in the serological tests.

The plant protein contaminant seems to be that known as 'fraction 1 protein' and, because of its tendency to polymerize, is liable to occur in virus pellets after high-speed centrifugation. A buffer such as citrate, Versene, or Tris should therefore be used to prevent aggregation of the virus and fraction 1 protein.

Methods of virus purification have been dealt with in Chapter Four, so they will only be mentioned again here. They are density-gradient centrifugation, agar-gel filtration (Ackers and Steere, 1962), and serological absorption; this latter method is particularly suitable for serological studies and the reader should consult Gold (1961) and Steere (1964). Another method used successfully for the removal of antigenic contaminants from plant virus preparations is zone electrophoresis (van Regenmortel, 1964, 1966 a and b).

It was pointed out by Bawden et al. (1936) and Stanley (1936) that infectivity and serological activity were not necessarily connected. In other words, viruses which had been inactivated, by ultraviolet light for example, still retained their serological activity unimpaired. In their studies of turnip yellow mosaic virus, Markham and Smith (1949) showed that the 'top' and 'bottom' components of a purified virus solution gave similar serological reactions, although the top component contained no RNA and was not infectious. The reason for this became clear when it was proved by Gierer and Schramm (1956) and by Fraenkel-Conrat (1956) that infectivity was confined to the nucleic acid alone. This means that serological assays measure only the virus protein. Bawden (1964) points out that the disagreements in measuring serological activity may reach the two extreme forms of: (a) preparations being highly infective but not reacting with virus antiserum; and (b) preparations being fully active serologically but not infective. Presumably, this means that here the two components of the virus particle are being separately assayed, the nucleic acid in (a) and the protein coat in (b).

## The Precipitin Reaction

There are four practical applications of the precipitin technique in the study of plant viruses: firstly, the identification of a virus; secondly, the detection of latent virus infections in plants; thirdly, the recognition of relationships between viruses which otherwise might not be suspected; and, fourthly, the quantitative estimation of viruses.

The rabbits used for preparing the antisera should be large (about 4 lb) and should preferably have fairly large ears with prominent veins; the variety of rabbit known as 'half-lops' is suitable. A 1-ml hypodermic syringe with a thin needle (about size 14) is used. The syringe is filled and air bubbles are expelled with the tip of the syringe held upright. The injection is made into the vein which runs along the upper surface of the ear, parallel to the hind edge and about $\frac{1}{8}$ to $\frac{3}{16}$ of an inch from it. It is useless to try to use the other veins even though they may appear larger.

If a rabbit is going to receive a series of injections, it is preferable to give the first near the tip of the ear and each later injection successively closer to the base.

About 2 weeks after injection, the rabbit is bled from the other ear; a small cut being made in the marginal vein near the base of the ear, using a small, very sharp scalpel. The cuts for later bleedings are made successively nearer the tip of the ear; the blood is collected in a tube and left for some hours to clot. The serum is poured off and centrifuged to remove any remaining blood cells. Antiserum prepared in this way is not sterile and will deteriorate unless stored under conditions which prevent bacterial growth.

The following is a brief description of the method used to carry out the precipitin test using a liquid medium. A convenient way is to use 1 ml samples of antiserum at a constant dilution in a series of test-tubes 7 mm in diameter, to each of which is added 1 ml of antigen solution at different dilutions. Serial dilutions by a factor of 2 are suitable, and both antiserum and virus should be diluted in normal saline (0·85 per cent NaCl) (Bawden, 1964).

The tubes are set up in racks in a water-bath with the temperature controlled at 50°C. Most suitable is a bath with windows in front and rear, with illumination from behind. The tubes can then be observed without removal from the bath. After the antiserum-antigen mixture has been added, the contents of each tube are mixed by brief shaking, and the lower half of the tube immersed in the water.

The tubes are then observed for the first appearance of a precipitate which gives the optimal precipitation point; the precipitation end-point is given, after a period of hours, by the tube with the most diluted antigen which contains a visible floccule.

Bawden and Pirie (1938) demonstrated that a rod-shaped virus such as TMV or potato virus X gave a bulky, flocculent precipitate as compared to the dense granular precipitate characteristic of a small isometric virus like that of tomato bushy stunt.

During the last decade, the precipitin test in a free liquid has been largely displaced by precipitin reactions in gel. Sometimes known as the plate test of Ouchterlony (1958), this consists of an agar gel in a circular holder, such as a Petri dish, with a number of wells made in the agar. These can be made by means of steel blocks inserted before the agar hardens or they can be cut out later with a cork borer.

Solutions put into wells tend to ooze under the agar, but this can be prevented by making the glass non-wettable by coating it with a few drops of silicone or formvar solution. During development of the precipitin reaction, the plates must be kept in a moist chamber to prevent changes due to drying, alternatively some liquid paraffin can be layered over the surface.

The diffusion of the two reactants towards each other eventually creates a zone in the agar where they meet in serologically optimal proportions, and it is along this line that antigen-antibody complexes will be formed (see Plate 15) (van Regenmortel, 1966).

## Some Results of the Application of Serological Methods

Bawden and Pirie (1937) showed that the viruses known as Cucumber Viruses 3 and 4 have certain antigens in common with tobacco mosaic virus, long before a common host plant was known on which cross-immunity tests could be carried out. The same workers (1942) demonstrated that the virus of tobacco necrosis is in reality a number of viruses, biologically similar but serologically different. This could hardly have been demonstrated in any other way because the lesions produced on infected plants by the different viruses are so much alike.

The precipitin method has been used to show relationships, hitherto quite unsuspected, among the nematode-transmitted viruses. *Arabis* mosaic, first described by Smith and Markham (1944), is now known to be due to a virus identical with, or closely related to, other viruses causing diseases of economic importance such as raspberry yellow dwarf, strawberry yellow crinkle, a disease of cherry trees, characterized by rasp-like excrescences on the leaves, and rhubarb mosaic. The same is true of the tomato black-ring virus (Smith 1946) which has been shown to be the same as that causing potato 'bouquet' disease, beet ringspot, and a disease of lettuce (Cadman, 1963; Harrison, 1957; Smith and Short, 1959).

Other examples are the relationships shown to exist between pea mosaic and bean yellow mosaic viruses (Brandes, 1964), *Sorghum* red stripe and sugar cane mosaic viruses (von Wechmar, 1966), *Odontoglossum* ringspot and tobacco mosaic viruses (Corbett, 1963).

Most of the results obtained by the application of serological techniques have been in relation to sap-transmissible viruses, but some work has been carried out on viruses which are only vector-transmitted.

Experiments on these lines have been made by Black and Brakke (1954). They purified wound-tumour virus by zonal centrifugation in sucrose solution density-gradient columns. The virus pellet was re-suspended in sodium chloride buffered with phosphate and emulsified with a mixture of Mayol F mineral oil and Arlacel A emulsifier. Rabbits were given 1 to 4 injections in the large muscles of the hind legs. Virus isolated from plants or from the leafhopper produced antisera reacting with purified virus from the opposite source at serum dilutions up to 1:1600, indicating common antigenic reactions for virus obtained from the two sources. Precipitin, complement-fixation, and specific neutralization reactions were demonstrated, the latter by injection of serum-virus mixtures into leafhopper vectors. It is considered that these techniques provide a rapid assay and means of determining relationships among some leafhopper-borne viruses.

### References

ACKERS, G. K. and STEERE, R. L. (1962) *Biochim. Biophys. Acta.* **32**, 140.

BALL, E. M. (1964) In *Plant Virology.* pp. 235–52. Eds. M. K. Corbett and H. D. Sisler. Gainesville: Univ. of Florida Press.

BAWDEN, F. C. (1964) *Plant Viruses and Virus Diseases.* 4th ed. p. 164. New York: Ronald Press Co.

BAWDEN, F. C. and PIRIE, N. W. (1937) *Brit. J. exp. Path.* **18**, 275.

BAWDEN, F. C. and PIRIE, N. W. (1938) *Brit. J. exp. Path.* **19**, 251.

BAWDEN, F. C. and PIRIE, N. W. (1942) *Brit. J. exp. Path.* **23**, 314.

BAWDEN, F. C., PIRIE, N. W., and SPOONER, E. T. C. (1936) *Brit. J. exp. Path.* **17**, 204.

BEALE, PURDY, H. (1928) *Proc. Soc. exp. Biol. N.Y.* **25**, 702.

BIRKELAND, J. M. (1934) *Bot. Gaz.* **95**, 419.

BLACK, L. M. and BRAKKE, M. K. (1954) *Phytopathology.* **44**, 482.

BRANDES, J. (1964) *Mitt. Biol. Bundesanstalt Land-Forstwirtsch.*, Berlin-Dahlem. **110**, 130.

CADMAN, C. H. (1963) *Ann. Rev. Phytopathol.* **1**, 143–72.

CORBETT, M. K. (1963) *Florida, Univ. Agric. Exptl. Sta. Ann. Rept.* p. 145.

FRAENKEL-CONRAT, H. (1956) *J. Amer. Chem. Soc.* **78**, 882.

GIERER, A. and SCHRAMM, G. (1956) *Nature.* **177**, 702.

GOLD, A. H. (1961) *Phytopathology.* **51**, 561.

GRATIA, A. (1933a) *C. R. Soc. Biol. Paris.* **114**, 923.

GRATIA, A. (1933b) *C. R. Soc. Biol. Paris.* **114**, 1382.

HARRISON, B. D. (1957) *Ann. appl. Biol.* **45**, 462.

MARKHAM, R. and SMITH, K. M. (1949) *Parasitology.* **39**, 330.

MATTHEWS, R. E. F. (1957) *Plant Virus Serology.* Cambridge Univ. Press.

MORITZ, O. (1964) In *Taxonomic Biochemistry and Serology.* Ed. C. A. Leone. p. 275. New York: Ronald Press Co.

OUCHTERLONY, Ö. (1958) *Progr. Allergy.* **6**, 30.

SMITH, K. M. (1946) *Parasitology.* **37**, 126–30.

SMITH, K. M. and MARKHAM, R. (1944) *Phytopathology.* **34**, 324–9.

SMITH, K. M. and SHORT, M. E. (1959) *Plant Pathol.* **8**, 54–6.

STANLEY, W. M. (1936) *Science.* **83**, 626.

STEERE, R. L. (1964) In *Plant Virology.* Eds. M. K. Corbett and H. D. Sisler. p. 211. Gainesville: Univ. of Florida Press.

VAN REGENMORTEL, M. H. V. (1964) *Phytopathology.* **54**, 282.

VAN REGENMORTEL, M. H. V. (1966) *Adv. Vir. Res.* **12**, 207–71.

VAN REGENMORTEL, M. H. V. (1966a) *Proc. Conf. Plant Viruses.* 1965. Wageningen. p. 213. Amsterdam: North-Holland Publishing Co.

VAN REGENMORTEL, M. H. V. (1966b) *Proc. Internat. Conf. Virus and Vectors on Perennial Hosts and Vitis.* 1965. Univ. California Div. Agric. Sci.

VON WECHMAR, B. M. (1966) D.Sc. Dissertation, University of Stellenbosch.

# CHAPTER TWELVE

# Tissue- and Cell-culture of Plant Viruses

Although viruses cannot be grown in a synthetic culture medium, the cell, which, after all, is the nurse to the virus, can be so propagated.

This procedure, loosely known as tissue-culture, affords great opportunities for the investigation of cell-virus relationships.

There are two types, *tissue-culture* and *cell-culture*: in the first, explants – pieces of tissue – are used, and, in the second, dispersed tissues or loose cells.

Most attention has been paid, so far, to the culture of various plant parts such as roots, endosperm, pollens, nucelli, and pieces of stem, and especially tobacco callus tissue. Various diseased tissues have also been used; these include the tumour induced by the wound tumour virus (WTV), crown-gall, and insect galls. Of the above, the root and stem apices are perhaps the easiest to cultivate.

## Plant Tissue-culture

White (1934) was the first to examine the possibilities of growing plant viruses in tissue-culture. He investigated the multiplication of tobacco and aucuba mosaic viruses in growing excised tomato root tips.

A tomato plant already systemically infected with the viruses was used and the stem was cut up into segments; these were thoroughly washed and were suspended by threads in 3-litre Erlenmeyer flasks containing a little water. The pieces of stem were kept out of contact with the water or the sides of the flask; the flasks were then plugged with cotton-wool and allowed to stand till roots developed. After 11 days, the root tips were removed and placed in 125-ml Erlenmeyer flasks; each flask contained 50 ml of nutrient medium as follows:

| | |
|---|---|
| Ca (NO$_3$)$_2$ | 0·60 millimols |
| MgSO$_4$ | 0·30 millimols |
| KNO$_3$ | 0·80 millimols |
| KCl | 0·87 millimols |
| KH$_2$PO$_4$ | 0·09 millimols |
| Fe$_2$(SO$_4$)$_3$ | 0·006 millimols |
| Sucrose | 2 per cent by weight |
| Yeast (extract) | 0·01 per cent |

At the end of a week, the surviving cultures were cut into pieces about 10 mm long. After further subculturing, a single root tip was selected as parent stock for all subsequent subcultures. It was found that the two viruses continued to multiply actively in growing isolated root tips for at least 25 to 30 weeks.

Using the above technique, the writer (unpublished) cultured the viruses of tobacco mosaic (TMV) and tobacco necrosis (TNV) in root tips of infected tobacco plants. To obtain roots infected with tobacco necrosis, pieces of roots from normal tobacco plants were ground up and tested for the presence of virus by inoculation to *Phaseolus vulgaris*, the test plant for TNV. The tobacco mosaic virus continued to multiply for several weeks, but after the fourth or fifth subculture no more TNV was detectable in the pieces of root.

Three plant tumours produced by the wound tumour virus have been isolated and grown in tissue culture. The first of these, R, was isolated by Black (1947, 1957) from tumours on the roots of virus-infected *Rumex acetosa*. The other two were isolated by Nickell (1955 a and b) from root and stem tumours. Burkholder and Nickell (1949) developed a basal medium on which the tissue made rapid growth. The composition is as follows: 2 per cent sucrose; 1 per cent agar; 0·002 M KNO$_3$; 0·003 M Ca(NO$_3$)$_2$; 0·008 M KH$_2$PO$_4$; 0·001 M MgSO$_4$; 0·003 M CaCl$_2$; 0·002 M KCl; 0·001 M MgCl$_2$; 100μg/l thiamin; 800μg/l pyridoxin; 800 μg/l niacinamide; 0·1 mg/l boron; 0·1 mg/l manganese; 0·3 mg/l zinc; 0·1 mg/l copper; 0·0 mg/l molybdenum; 0·5 mg/l iron.

The wound tumour virus does not seem to continue to multiply indefinitely. Black (1965) points out that, although the original cultured sorrel tumour tissue infected two sorrel plants with wound-tumour, when grafted back to them after a period of 11 months in culture, recent attempts to repeat this after longer periods in culture have been un-successful. Black has also failed to detect any virus in extracts of the tissues by serological tests or by infectivity tests using the insect-injection techniques.

Hildebrandt *et al.* (1946) have studied the influence of the composition of the medium on growth *in vitro* of excised tobacco and sunflower tissue-cultures. In general, the tissues grew on a wide range of concentrations of the salts tested, but best growth appeared when the concentration of various items among the nutrients were increased over those of the basal medium (White, 1943). For example, excellent growth of tobacco cultures occurred when the concentrations were increased of sodium sulphate, calcium nitrate, sodium dihydrogen phosphate, iron, zinc sulphate, and potassium iodide. Similar good growths of sunflower cultures were obtained, when the concentrations were increased of calcium nitrate, magnesium sulphate, potassium nitrate, potassium chloride, sodium dihydrogen phosphate, iron, zinc sulphate, boric acid, and glycine.

Kassanis (1957) has investigated the nutritional requirements of cultured tobacco-callus tissue and found that increasing the phosphate content of the tissue increased its growth but diminished the virus content, and this diminution was greater at a higher concentration of glucose. Mishra *et al.* (1964) consider that results suggest that under uniform conditions the virus content of the cultured tissues is not influenced by their growth. Some substances affect the growth of the tissue and some its virus concentration and there seems no correlation between the two effects.

## Modes of Infection of Tissue-cultures

Since it is rather difficult to infect plant tissue-cultures with viruses *de novo*, it is better, whenever possible, to start the culture with tissues from systemically infected plants. However, this is not always possible, and various methods, some of them ingenious, have been employed to bring about infection of the tissue-culture itself.

Kassanis *et al.* (1958) used four methods to infect normal and conditioned tobacco-callus growths and tomato root-cultures. They poured inoculum on the cultured tissue, soaked the cultured tissue in the inoculum, pricked the inoculum into the tissue by means of pins, and rubbed the tissue with a microspatula. The results varied somewhat, according to the method used, infection was occasionally brought about without injury or by superficial damage, but such tissues usually became virus-free after an interval. More permanent infection resulted from the deeper injuries caused by the pin-prick method. Similar lasting infection was produced in cultured tomato roots by the use of quartz powder as an abrasive (Bergmann, 1959; Bergmann and Melchers, 1959).

Sometimes it is possible to use the natural vector of a virus to infect cultured tissue, and this has been accomplished with two viruses, one sap-transmissible and the other not transmissible by this means. In the first case, tobacco necrosis virus was inoculated to tobacco-callus tissues by zoospores of the fungus *Olpidium brassicae*. Two strains of tobacco necrosis virus and three isolates of *O. brassicae* were used. 1 day before inoculation the tissues were transferred to small filter-paper cups pushed into vials 2 × 1 inch containing 5 ml Hoagland's solution diluted 1:20. The solution just touched the bottom of the paper cup, which was used to prevent the callus cells being lost in the liquid. The method of inoculation was to add to each vial 1 ml of Hoagland's solution containing zoospores and 0·5 ml containing purified virus. 4 or 5 days after inoculation, the virus in the tissues and in the fluid beneath them was assayed by infectivity tests on French beans (*Phaseolus vulgaris*).

All three isolates of *Olpidium* transmitted both strains of TNV to the tobacco-callus tissue (Kassanis and MacFarlane, 1964).

In the second case, where the virus is not sap-transmissible and is dependent upon a specific insect vector for its transfer to healthy tissues, a method has been developed for the inoculation of plant tissue cultures. The method requires aseptically reared insect vectors, obtained from surface-sterilized eggs and maintained on plants grown from sterilized seed in culture tubes with agar medium. Virus-infected plants were obtained by placing free-grown viruliferous insects on a portion of a plant protruding from the culture tube. The contaminated portion was later cut off, and the aseptically grown diseased plant was colonized by aseptic insects. When these insects became infective, they were placed on plant tissues *in vitro*. The virus of aster yellows was successfully transmitted, using this method, by means of the leaf hopper *Macrosteles fascifrons* Stål. to carrot tissue from which it was recovered after 50 days (Mitsuhashi and Maramorosch, 1964).

It is of interest to record here the reverse experiment in which a plant virus was successfully propagated in tissue-cultures of the leafhopper vector. Working with wound-tumour virus, Chiu *et al.* (1966) infected tissue-cultures derived from the vector insect *Agallia constricta* (Van Duzee) and were able to detect the infection by staining with fluorescein-conjugated antibody, and by infectivity tests. These criteria of infection are said to be specific and unequivocal and the experiments demonstrate multiplication of the wound-tumour virus in the inoculated tissues of the leafhopper.

## Cell-culture

Not much work has been published so far on the propagation of plant viruses in cell culture. Hildebrandt (1958) describes a technique for obtaining clones of single cell origin. Single-cell cultures were secured under aseptic conditions by spreading liquid or agar tissue cultures on sterile agar in a Petri dish. The single, isolated cells were picked up with a microspatula by hand under a dissecting microscope. The cell was then transferred to an 8 mm square of sterile filter paper in a Petri dish. The filter paper square had been placed 3 to 4 days previously on the established host-mother tissue-culture, so that it had absorbed a favour-able balance of nutrients from the culture. The filter-paper raft was then placed over the established tissue-culture and allowed to re-main until the single cell had divided sufficiently to be transferred to agar.

A method of isolating tobacco-leaf cells capable of supporting virus multiplication has been employed, based on the enzymatic degradation of the intercellular pectic substances by pectinase. The laminar tissue of leaves of *Nicotiana tabacum* were cut into strips of about 3 mm and shaken at room temperature for 3 to 4 hours in a 0·1 M Sörensen's phosphate buffer at pH 6·2 containing 0·35 moles of sucrose per litre and 0·2 per cent pectinase.

The separation of cells is dependent on vigorous shaking and occurs at the cut surfaces of the leaf pieces. When the shaking is completed, the isolated cells sink to the bottom while the remaining leaf debris remains in suspension or floats to the surface. The supernatant is then poured off and replaced by some of the sucrose, containing buffer but no pectinase. Centrifugation and resuspension are continued until the supernatant clears; final resuspension is achieved by drawing the cells into a pipette to separate any clumps of cells resulting from the centrifugation (Zaitlin, 1959).

Quite a number of different plant viruses have now been propagated in cultured tissues. In addition to those already mentioned, chilli mosaic virus (Mishra, 1963), sunhemp mosaic virus (Raychaudhuri et al., 1962), and a ringspot strain of potato virus X (Sharma and Raychaudhuri, 1962), and a type strain of TMV have been successfully cultivated in normal callus tissue obtained from virus-affected White Burley tobacco plants (Raychaudhuri and Mishra, 1962, 1965). Augier de Montgremier et al. (1948) grew callus from tobacco plants infected with tobacco and cucumber mosaic viruses and found that these two viruses retained their virulence for over a year in serial cultures. As techniques improve, no doubt more and more plant viruses will be successfully cultured either in plant parts or in single-cell clones.

Although this aspect of plant virology is still largely undeveloped, it offers great possibilities.

Apart from examination on the electron microscope of virus-infected cells, opportunity is afforded for the study of nutritional and environmental requirements, the effect of growth regulators, chemotherapy, and radiation. For a comprehensive review of these aspects, the reader is referred to Raychaudhuri (1966). A book by White (1963) on the cultivation of animal and plant cells should also be consulted.

### References

AUGIER DE MONTGREMIER, H., LIMASSET, P., and MOREL, G. (1948) Compt. Rend. 227, 606.

BERGMANN, L. (1959) Trans. N.Y. Acad. Sci. 21, 227.

BERGMANN, L. and MELCHERS, G. (1959) Z. Naturforsch. 14a, 73.

BLACK, L. M. (1947) Growth. (Suppl.) 6, 79.

BLACK, L. M. (1957) J. nat. Cancer Inst. 19, 663–78.

BLACK, L. M. (1965) in Handbuch der Pflanzenphysiologie. pp. 236–66. Ed. W. Ruhland. 15. 2. Berlin: Springer Verlag.

BURKHOLDER, P. R. and NICKELL, L. G. (1949) Bot. Gaz. 110, 426–37.

CHIU, REN-JONG, REDDY, D. V. R., and BLACK, L. M. (1966) Virology. 30, 562–6.

HILDEBRANDT, A. C. (1958) Proc. Natl. Acad. Sci. U.S. 44, 354.

HILDEBRANDT, A. C., RIKER, A. J., and DUGGAR, B. M. (1946) *Amer. J. Botany*. **33**, 591.

KASSANIS, B. (1957) *Virology*. **4**, 5.

KASSANIS, B. and MACFARLANE, I. (1964) *Nature*. **201**, 218.

KASSANIS, B., TINSLEY, T. W., and QUAK, F. (1958) *Ann. appl. Biol.* **46**, 11.

MISHRA, M. D. (1963) *Indian J. Microbiol*. **3**, 79.

MISHRA, M. D., RAYCHAUDHURI, S. P., and PHATAK, H. C. (1964) 'Symposium on Host-Parasite Relationships'. *Indian Phytopathol. Soc. Bull*. **2**, 18.

MITSUHASHI, J. and MARAMOROSCH, K. (1964) *Virology*. **23**, 277.

NICKELL, L. G. (1955a) *Année Biol*. [3]. **31**, 107.

NICKELL, L. G. (1955b) In *Antimetabolites and Cancer*. Ed. C. P. Rhoads. pp. 120–51. Washington, D.C.: Amer. Ass. Adv. Sci.

RAYCHAUDHURI, S. P. (1966) *Adv. Vir. Res*. **12**, 175–206.

RAYCHAUDHURI, S. P. and MISHRA, M. D. (1962) *Indian Phytopathol*. **15**, 185.

RAYCHAUDHURI, S. P. and MISHRA, M. D. (1965) *Indian Phytopathol*. **18**, 50.

RAYCHAUDHURI, S. P., NARIANI, T. K., and DAS, C. R. (1962) *Indian Phytopathol*. **15**, 79.

SHARMA, D. C. and RAYCHAUDHURI, S. P. (1962) *Indian Phytopathol*. **15**, 250.

WHITE, P. R. (1934) *Plant Physiol*. **9**, 585.

WHITE, P. R. (1943) *A Handbook of Plant Tissue Culture*. Lancaster, Pa: Cattell.

WHITE, P. R. (1963) *The Cultivation of Animal and Plant Cells*. New York: Ronald Press Co.

ZAITLIN, M. (1959) *Nature*. **184**, 1002–3.

K

# CHAPTER THIRTEEN

# Testing for Viruses: Indicator Plants

Since the very early days of plant virus study, virologists have sought for an alternative host plant when studying new or suspected viruses, especially those which are sap-transmissible. The ideal alternative host is one which reacts promptly and characteristically to sap-inoculation, preferably with the formation of local lesions on the inoculated leaves (see Chapter Ten). Such a plant has become known as a 'differential host' or 'indicator plant'.

The uses of indicator plants are many and they have become an important tool in plant virus research. Firstly, they may be used to confirm the presence of a virus in another plant which has vague or indeterminate symptoms. Secondly, they are invaluable for detecting latent virus infections: viruses which may be carried without symptoms by some plants often produce overt symptoms when transmitted to another plant. Thirdly, they can be used to indicate the presence of virus complexes and to separate the component viruses. Plants of this type have also been called 'filter plants' (Smith, 1931) because they filter out a component of a complex by virtue of immunity to one of them. In addition, they can be used to separate strains of the same virus occurring together in one plant (Johnson, 1947; Matthews, 1949). Fourthly, by their characteristic reactions, it is often possible to identify a virus which may be well known already but may be effectually disguised by its infection of an unusual or uncommon host plant. Fifthly, a good indicator plant allows the quantitative study of a virus by virtue of its formation of local lesions without systemic spread. Sixthly, by the capacity of indicator plants to reveal latent infection, they have come to play an important part in horticulture and in agriculture in what is known as the 'indexing' of crops. By this means, it is possible to gain an idea of the percentage of virus infection in a given crop, and such indexing is particularly useful in testing potatoes and stone-fruit trees for the presence of latent virus infections.

James Johnson (1925), one of the pioneers of plant virus research, was also one of the first to use an indicator plant. He inoculated young tobacco plants from apparently healthy potato plants and found that they became infected with what was at first known as the 'healthy potato virus' but which is now universally known as 'potato virus X'. The tobacco plant, together with *Datura stramonium*, was also used extensively at Cambridge in the early work on potato viruses. Tobacco seems to be susceptible to more viruses than any other known plant, and in plant virology it occupies a place comparable to the small 'laboratory animal' of those concerned with viruses of the higher animals.

There is now in use in plant virology a very large number of indicator plants, some of which have been developed or evolved for detecting a particular virus, while others are general-purpose plants and react to inoculation with many different viruses.

An ideal indicator plant is one which is easily and rapidly grown, has large leaves suitable for inoculation and, above all, reacts with the formation of local lesions on the inoculated leaf. It is better that the lesions should remain discrete without coalescing and that systemic infection should not follow.

One of the earliest indicator plants to be used, after the tobacco plant, was a related species *Nicotiana glutinosa*, and it is especially suitable for use with tobacco mosaic virus. It reacts with clear, discrete local lesions which are easily countable and do not spread or run together. Its place is gradually being taken now by varieties of tobacco, *N. tabacum*, which have been specially bred for this work. The gene governing the localization of the virus in *N. glutinosa* has been transferred to the tobacco plant, and special varieties of *N. tabacum* such as *xanthi* are much in use.

In North America, the bean (*Phaseolus vulgaris*), vars. Pinto, Golden Cluster, and others, is also much used as a local lesion host for tobacco mosaic virus. In England, beans are not suitable for work with this virus, since, in the writer's experience, the English varieties rarely react to form local lesions.

For some reason most of the best 'general purpose' indicator plants are found in the Chenopodiaceae, the first of these to be used being

*Gomphrena globosa*, which was shown by Wilkinson and Blodgett (1948) to be an excellent indicator for potato virus X. Another one is *Chenopodium amaranticolor*, first used by Bennett in California and later developed by Hollings (1956, 1957). This plant reacts with local lesions to infection by many viruses and it is not always easy to differentiate the various lesions and to correlate them with the causative virus.

In a more recent publication, Hollings (1966) has given an account of local-lesion- and other test-plants for the identification and culture of viruses; the following details are quoted from his work. Of *Chenopodium amaranticolor* and *C. quinoa*, the former is more suitable for work with polyhedral viruses and the latter for many filamentous viruses. These include the bean yellow mosaic, carnation vein mottle, and clover yellow vein viruses.

*Tetragonia expansa* (Aizoaceae), New Zealand spinach, reacts with large chlorotic to semi-necrotic local lesions to many aphid-borne filamentous viruses such as those of bean yellow mosaic, cabbage black ringspot, and sugar-beet mosaic, also chrysanthemum virus B and potato virus Y.

It should be remembered that both *T. expansa* and *C. amaranticolor* contain virus inhibitors (see Chapter Ten). *Gomphrena globosa* produces lesions with many viruses but the lesions tend to be rather large in relation to the leaf area. This limits the usefulness of the species for assay work. There is little inhibitory effect.

*Atriplex hortensis* was found to be susceptible to 30 out of 40 viruses tested. The purple leaf form was found to be more vigorous than the pale green type.

*Emilia sagittata* was infected by 32 out of 55 viruses tested. The principal use of this plant is for the culture and identification of some orchid viruses such as those of *Cymbidium* mosaic and ringspot and the orchid strain of tobacco mosaic virus.

In the Cruciferae, Chinese cabbage, *Brassica chinensis*, is useful for culturing the viruses of cauliflower mosaic and turnip yellow mosaic (Plate 1.).

There are more test plants in the Solanaceae than in any other family; two species of *Nicotiana* have already been mentioned, but *N. clevelandii* is a good local lesion host for several nematode-transmitted viruses such as those of tobacco ringspot, tomato ringspot, tomato black-ring and cherry leaf-roll. *N. clevelandii* is susceptible to many viruses which seem not to affect other Solanaceous plants.

In the Leguminosae, the French bean, *Phaseolus vulgaris*, and the cowpea, *Vigna sinensis*, are generally susceptible to polyhedral and nematode-transmitted viruses. *V. sinensis* was the original indicator plant for the virus of tomato bushy stunt (Smith, 1935).

Of species of *Trifolium*, *T. incarnatum* is the most susceptible and reacts to the viruses of bean yellow mosaic, pea mosaic, red clover mottle, and clover yellow vein.

Lovisolo (1966) suggests basil, *Ocimum basilicum*, as a test plant for a strain of tomato bushy stunt and tobacco necrosis viruses. It seems more susceptible to infection by isometric rather than anisometric viruses.

By means of these indicator and test plants, it should be possible to gain much information about an unknown virus. The first necessity, of course, is that the virus is sap-transmissible; if it is not, the vector must be identified and the symptomatology and host range established. With a sap-transmissible virus, however, information can be obtained on the host range, symptomatology, and local lesion hosts. Ross (1964) points out that it is important to establish that only one virus is present. One way to do this is to inoculate to a series of plants and then inoculate back to the original plant species to see if the symptoms are the same. An analysis of a potato virus complex by the use of differential hosts was first made by Smith (1931). If two viruses are present, there are many simple means of separation in addition to the foregoing; these are dilution end-point, longevity *in vitro*, thermal inactivation point (see Chapter Four), insect transmission, and differential rates of movement in the newly infected plant. When a tobacco plant is infected with a mixture of potato viruses X and Y, the latter virus travels more quickly to the growing point and can be obtained in pure culture by inoculation from the youngest leaves as soon as they show the characteristic 'clearing of the veins' (Smith, 1931).

Useful information on relationships can sometimes be obtained by interaction with other viruses. There is the cross-protection test, used by Kunkel (1934); this is the half-leaf test when one of the viruses induces local lesions in a host susceptible to both, while the other does not.

Another sign of unrelatedness is the increased severity of the disease caused by two viruses as compared to that produced by each virus acting independently (synergism). This is well illustrated by the lethal disease of tomatoes, 'glasshouse streak' so-called, caused by tobacco mosaic virus and potato virus X acting in unison.

Ross (1964) suggests the following criteria to use in establishing the identity of an unknown.

*Group I.* Chemical and physical properties of the virus particles, serological properties, and response to genetic change in the host.

*Group II.* Ability to cross-protect, stability *in vitro*, general transmission characteristics, and interaction in simultaneous infections.

*Group III.* Symptomatology and host range.

This is perhaps a policy of perfection. At the same time it is not safe to rely on too few characteristics. For example, sub-inoculation from local lesions carried on for a year or more is not sufficient evidence that the agent is of a viral nature (Smith, 1951; Yarwood *et al.*, 1961).

## References

HOLLINGS, M. (1956) *Plant Path.* **5**, 57–60.

HOLLINGS, M. (1957) *Plant Path.* **6**, 133–5.

HOLLINGS, M. (1966) in *Viruses of Plants.* pp. 230–41. Eds. A. B. R. Beemster and J. Dijkstra. Amsterdam: North-Holland Publishing Co.

JOHNSON, J. (1925) *Wisc. Agric. Exp. Sta. Res. Bull.* No. 63.

JOHNSON, J. (1947) *Phytopathology.* **37**, 822–37.

KUNKEL, L. O. (1934) *Phytopathology.* **24**, 437.

LOVISOLO, O. (1966) in *Viruses of Plants.* pp. 242–6. Eds. A. B. R. Beemster and J. Dijkstra. Amsterdam: North-Holland Publishing Co.

MATTHEWS, R. E. F. (1949) *Parasitology.* **39**, 241–4.

ROSS, A. F. (1964) in *Plant Virology.* pp. 68–92. Eds. M. K. Corbett and H. D. Sisler. Gainesville: Univ. of Florida Press.

SMITH, K. M. (1931) *Proc. roy. Soc. B.* **109**, 251–67.

SMITH, K. M. (1935) *Ann. appl. Biol.* **22**, 731.

SMITH, K. M. (1951) *Nature.* **167**, 1061.

WILKINSON, R. E. and BLODGETT, F. M. (1948) *Phytopathology.* (Abstr.) **38**, 28.

YARWOOD, C. E., RESCONICH, E. C., ARK, P. A., SCHLEGEL, D. E., and SMITH, K. M. (1961) *Plant Dis. Reptr.* **45**, 85.

# CHAPTER FOURTEEN

# Nomenclature and Classification. Control

## Nomenclature and Classification

There is no doubt that some sort of system is urgently needed to arrange in order the 300 or so plant viruses already described and to reduce the chaos that exists at present.

The problem of the nomenclature and classification of viruses in general, and of plant viruses in particular, has been a controversial subject for many years. James Johnson was among the first to attempt an orderly arrangement of plant viruses by naming the virus after its most common or original host plant; for example, tobacco mosaic virus became tobacco virus 1. Smith (1937) adapted and enlarged this system to apply to all plant viruses known at that time. The Latin generic name of the plant was used instead of the English popular name and tobacco mosaic virus was called *Nicotiana Virus* 1, potato virus X became *Solanum Virus* 1, and so forth. This system worked fairly well for a time till the increasing numbers of viruses associated with one plant genus, particularly the potato and the tobacco plants, rendered the numbering system impractical. In the second edition of *A Textbook of Plant Virus Diseases*, Smith (1957) reverted to the use of the common English names of the virus diseases most of which were used by the *Review of Applied Mycology* in their published list. In 1939 and 1948, Holmes grouped the viruses according to the main symptoms formed in the plant and instituted a Latin binomial system. Mosaic diseases were grouped under *Marmor* and tobacco mosaic virus was called *Marmor tabaci*.

Of all the characteristics on which to base any kind of nomenclature,

the symptomatology is the least reliable not only because it brings together in one group very different viruses but because one virus can
produce quite different diseases according to the host plant, environmental conditions, and so forth.

Any sound system of classification must be based upon the fundamental characteristics of the virus itself, which are independent of the
host.

This has been attempted by Brandes and Bercks (1965), who classified all plant viruses which were elongated rods. Using this morphological character, combined with serological relationships, they arranged the elongated plant viruses into 6 different groups using the
name of one well-known representative to characterize each group as
follows.

(1) Tobacco rattle virus group.

(2) Tobacco mosaic virus group.

(3) Potato virus X group.

(4) Potato virus S group.

(5) Potato virus Y group.

(6) Beet yellows virus group.

Bawden (1964) stipulates that, in attempting any groupings that un-
doubtedly reflect intrinsic characters of viruses, criteria must come from
information independent of features in which the host might play a
part, i.e. they must come from such things as particle morphology,
chemical constitution, and stability *in vitro*.

He points out that much of the present confusion arises from the
multiplicity of virus strains, many of which have been described as new
viruses and given new names.

Mayr (1953) has suggested, for groups of clones that have probably
derived from a common ancestor, the name 'collective species'. Bawden
favours this idea and says that, for allocating strains to a collective
species, the one criterion that seems of outstanding value is serological
relationship. All viruses so far found to be closely related antigenically
also resemble one another in other such intrinsic properties as particle
morphology and chemical composition, not only ratio of nucleic acid
to protein but also the relative proportions in which the four nucleotides occur in their nucleic acid.

The first step required for classifying plant viruses is to select a specific strain to act as the type for each collective species and to prepare an antiserum against it.

In Chapter Eleven, it was shown that the serological reactions of plant viruses arose only from the protein coat of the virus particle without reference to the nucleic acid. This, as Bawden points out, raises difficulties in dealing with viruses which are defective in forming their protein coat.

In any case it seems to the writer no easy matter to classify threads of nucleic acid.

At the time of writing, two systems of nomenclature and classification have been put forward, one of these favours the Latin binomial system and the other does not. The first seems to be founded on a system put forward by Lwoff *et al.* (1962) and is based on the structure of the virus particle (virion). They consider that the use of four features permits the classification of viruses. These four features, called 'essential integrants' are the following.

(1) Genetic material, DNA or RNA.

(2) Symmetry of the virus: helical, cubical, or binal (binal applies to those bacterial viruses which possess two different symmetrical structures, the 'head' and the 'tail').

(3) Nucleocapsid: naked or enveloped. (The structure composed of the nucleic acid surrounded by the capsid is the nucleocapsid.)

(4) Quantitative data: diameter of the nucleocapsid for virions with helical symmetry and number of capsomeres for the virion with cubical symmetry.

This system appears to be the basis for the first of the two systems of nomenclature mentioned above. It has been recommended by the Provisional Committee of Nomenclature of Viruses (PCNV) and has been outlined by Pereira (1966) as follows.

(1) Viruses of animals, plants, and bacteria should be gathered into a single phylum, *Vira*.

(2) The phylum should be divided into sub-phyla, classes, orders, families, genera, and species, these divisions being by necessity arbitrary and not equivalent to taxa of other phyla.

(3) Genera should have Latin or Latinized Greek names ending in 'virus'. Each genus is typified by a well-authenticated species to be deposited in international culture collections.

(4) Each family should be named after a type genus to which the suffix *idae* is added.

(5) The code should not include a law of priority. A list of *nomina conservanda* in which virus names in general use are maintained whenever possible is submitted for approval by the International Committee of Nomenclature of Viruses.

(6) Taxa designated after personal names, anagrams, siglas, hybrids of names, or nonsense names should not be acceptable.

(7) New names to be adopted must be submitted to the International Committee of Nomenclature through its Judicial Commission.

*Classification.* The four characters suggested are those already mentioned: type of nucleic acid; symmetry of the virion, presence or absence of envelope; dimensions. They are adopted in this hierarchical order to divide the phylum into sub-phyla, orders, classes, families, and genera.

The alternative system put forward by Gibbs *et al.* (1966) does not attempt to treat viruses as conventional organisms. It is based on Adansonian principles, a method of grouping together organisms that have the most features in common (Adanson, 1757). Viruses would be designated by vernacular trivial names followed by a cryptogram containing information available or not on a number of unweighted characters.

The cryptogram suggested takes the following form – tobacco mosaic virus: R/1, 2/5, E/E, S/O; where the symbols have the following meaning.

| 1st term | Type of nucleic acid: R, RNA; D, DNA. Strandedness: 1, single; 2, double. |
|---|---|
| 2nd term | Molecular weight of nucleic acid in millions/percentage of nucleic acid in infective particles. |
| 3rd term | Outline of particle/outline of nuclear capsid: S, essentially spherical; E, elongated with parallel sides, ends not rounded; U, elongated with parallel sides, end(s) rounded; X, complex or none of above. |

4th term

Kinds of host infected/kinds of vector.

Kinds of host: V, vertebrate; I, invertebrate; S, seed plant; F, fungus; B, bacterium; A, Actinomycete.

Kinds of vector: O, spreads without a vector; Ac, mites and ticks (Acarina, Arachnida); Al, white fly (Aleyrodidae, Hemiptera, Insecta); Ap, aphid (Aphididae, Hemiptera, Insecta); Au, leaf-, plant-, or tree-hopper (Auchenorrhyncha, Hemiptera); Cc, mealy-bug (Coccidae, Hemiptera); Cl, beetle (Coleoptera); Di, flies and mosquitoes (Diptera); Fu, fungus (Chytridiales, Plasmodiophorales, Fungi); Gy, Mirid, Piesmid or Tingid bug (Gymnocerata); Ne, nematode (Nematoda); Ps, Psyllid (Psyllidae, Hemiptera); Si, flea (Siphonaptera); Th, thrips (Thysanoptera); Ve, vector(s) known but none of above.

The drawback to this system as applied to plant viruses at present is the lack of the necessary data to fill in the cryptograms.

It will be noticed that neither of these systems incorporates the serological relationships of viruses.

## Control

There are various methods of approach to the problem of the control of plant virus diseases; or, to put it in another way, to prevent the spread of plant viruses. They are not, of course, all applicable in the same way to the various diseases. These methods can be classified roughly under the following six headings, and the applications of each of them to specific virus diseases will be briefly discussed.

(1) Elimination of the sources of virus infection.

(2) Avoiding the vectors.

(3) Direct attack on the vectors.

(4) Breeding resistant varieties of crops.

(5) Cure of virus-infected plants.

(6) Special methods of propagation.

To these may perhaps be added the 'vaccination' of a plant with an avirulent or masked strain of a virus which thereby sometimes immunizes the plant against a more severe strain of the same virus but not of course against a different virus. This method is at present largely academic.

## Elimination of the Sources of Virus Infection

*Wild Host Plants.* Two fairly recent discoveries have emphasized the importance of weeds as sources of virus infection. One is the implication of nematode worms as vectors of several viruses affecting raspberry and strawberry plants; the other is the fact that these viruses are transmitted through the seed of many common weeds which carry the viruses without symptoms. This is doubly important owing to the fact that the over-wintering nematodes lose their infectivity but regain it in the spring from germinating infective weed seeds (Murant and Taylor, 1965). The survival of the virus through the winter is thus ensured.

Various surveys, quoted by Broadbent (1964), have been made on the frequency with which wild plants become infected with viruses and thus act as sources of infection for cultivated crops. MacClement and Richards (1956) in Canada tested the sap from five species of wild plants from six different areas of the Royal Botanical Gardens, Ontario. They found that about 10 per cent of all the plants were infected, often with more than one virus; the viruses identified included those of sugar-beet curly-top, cucumber mosaic, and tomato spotted wilt. In a similar survey near Berlin, Schwarz (1959) found that cucumber mosaic, cabbage black-ringspot, lucerne mosaic, and potato Y viruses were common. Of these the first two seem to have been the most widespread.

It has been pointed out by Varney (1967) that relatively little attention has been paid to woody shrubs and trees as reservoirs of viruses that infect herbaceous crop plants. For example, tomato ringspot and tobacco ringspot viruses, both nematode-transmitted, occur respectively in wild as well as cultivated elm (*Ulmus americana*) and in blueberry (*Vaccinium corymbosum*).

*Cultivated Crops.* Viruses which have a fairly wide host range can be brought to one crop from another cultivated crop. For example, clover is the host of several viruses which affect peas and beans; moreover, the chief aphid vector, *Macrosiphum pisi*, over-winters on clover. It is unwise therefore, to grow perennial leguminous crops in close proximity to susceptible annual crops. The virus of cucumber mosaic is one which lurks in many perennial garden plants, dahlias, pentstemon, lupins, delphiniums, *Buddleia*, and even in privet hedges. There is thus always virus at hand ready to attack vegetable marrows or out-door cucumbers, on both of which it causes a crippling disease.

Remnants of the previous year's crop are frequently important sources of virus. 'Volunteer' potatoes and sugar-beet, which are usually infected with one or more viruses, are good examples. Mangold clamps, too, are liable to be reservoirs of the beet-yellows virus.

At one time it was the practice to grow the steckling, or seed-plant, sugar-beets alongside, or close to, the root crops. The effect of this was that the seed-plants became infected with virus-yellows in the autumn; the aphid vectors wintered on these plants and, the following spring, infected the new season's beet crop over very large areas. Now some attempt is being made to grow the seed-beets in isolation from the root crops and so to keep the latter free of virus.

With vegetatively propagated crops such as strawberries, raspberries, potatoes, and bulb plants, it is supremely important to start with a virus-free crop. The foundation of good crops of potatoes is the use of good quality virus-free 'seed', since it is essential to start the crop with as little virus in it as possible; otherwise there will be a source of virus ready to hand within the crop. Having obtained a stock of clean 'seed', it should be grown as far as possible from second-rate potatoes. All the advantages of virus-free 'seed' will be lost if the crop is grown alongside home-saved 'seed'.

Another important point is careful attention to roguing out any obviously virus-diseased plants and also any ground-keepers which are usually a prolific source of virus infection. Roguing should be done as early as possible while the plants are still small; there are several reasons for this. There will have been less time for the virus to spread from the infected plants, no tubers will have been formed and small plants are easily disposed of.

*Avoiding the Vectors*

This can be achieved in various ways, by isolation, by breaking the cycle of vector, virus, and host plant, and by artificial barriers to exclude the

vector. The growing of seed-potatoes in particular areas of Scotland
and Ireland is a practical illustration on a large scale of the control of
potato virus diseases by avoiding the vector. The climate of the Scotch
and Irish seed-growing districts is too cool and moist for the aphid
*Myzus persicae*, the chief vector, which does not thrive if the temperature is lower than about 65°F, and if relative humidity is more than 75
per cent. Similarly, in some tropical countries it is possible to raise
virus-free seed potatoes in areas where the temperature is too high for
the aphid to exist.

Investigation of the life history of the chief potato aphid, *M. persicae*,
shows that this insect can be partially avoided even in England. There
are three possible ways in which this aphid can pass the winter; as an
egg on the peach tree, in glasshouses, and, in mild winters, out-of-doors
on brassica crops, particularly brussels sprouts. Whenever practicable,
therefore, potato crops should be grown in areas where *M. persicae*
cannot find these facilities for over-wintering.

Sometimes it is possible to avoid a bad infestation of an aphid vector
by early sowing. Thus, early sowing of the commercial sugar-beet crop
is recommended because it avoids the infestation by *M. persicae* of the
very young beet plants, and allows them to be more advanced before the
appearance of the aphid.

Breaking the crop cycle, when practicable, is an efficient method of
control. It was successfully applied in the case of a white-fly-transmitted
virus of tobacco, known as leaf-curl. The white-fly bred on infected
suckers from the previous year's tobacco crop but a fallow period of 3
weeks after the destruction of all the crop controlled the disease
(Hopkins, 1932). Broadbent (1964) also quotes the control of western
celery mosaic in the U.S.A. by means of a celery-free period of 3 to 5
months during the summer, adopted by agreement with the growers
(Severin and Freitag, 1938). There is much evidence that over-wintering
sugar-beet and mangold seed crops are the important winter reservoir
of the two viruses which cause sugar-beet yellows. Ribbands (1962)
considers that the way to tackle this disease is to eliminate the seed crop.
If seed crops of sugar-beet and mangolds were grown, throughout
Britain, only in alternate years, the virus cycle would be broken and the
disease controlled.

It is perhaps significant that in those states of the U.S.A. where there is a period when no sugar-beets are grown, in other words a break in the crop cycle, virus-yellows is of little importance.

The condition of the plant itself may play some part in determining the degree of infestation by aphids, and Kennedy (1958) has shown that some aphids prefer the old leaves to the younger for colonization. Even the colour of the plant may play a part, since three times as many aphids alighted on green or yellow lettuce plants as on brown ones, and the brown variety, in consequence, is less frequently infected with lettuce mosaic than the green or yellow varieties (Müller, 1956).

A more positive method of avoiding vectors, particularly flying insects like aphids and leafhoppers, is to ward them off the crop by means of screens or cages. This has been done in the U.S.A. against the leafhoppers which spread the virus causing 'aster-yellows'. Two types of shield have been tested: one consisted of cloth-covered sidewalls or fences without tops, but these were found commercially unsatisfactory; in the second type, cloth-covered cages or houses were employed. The tops and sides of the enclosures were completely covered with cloth not coarser than 22 by 22 threads per inch. It might be worth while experimenting with some such device to protect young cauliflower or other brassica seedlings, since it is in the seed bed, before the plants are set out in the field, that much infection with aphid-borne viruses takes place.

A living screen or 'barrier crop' is sometimes effective; this is usually a rapidly growing plant like the Jerusalem artichoke; but sunflowers, oats, maize, or barley have also been used. Broadbent and Martini (1959) interplanted rows of cereal plants at intervals to ward off mosaic from cauliflower seedlings.

Simons (1957, 1960) has used sunflower barriers to ward off aphid-borne viruses, particularly potato virus Y, from pepper, celery, and tomato crops. Most effective were 50-ft-wide strips of non-susceptible crops around the fields; spraying the barriers with parathion increased their efficacy.

*Direct Attack on the Vectors*
Much progress has been made lately in the control of the aphid-borne viruses affecting the potato crop by means of insecticides. Broadbent and his co-workers (1956, 1958) have shown that good results can be

obtained by this method, especially as regards potato leaf-roll. It is not sufficient to kill the aphids which have been bred in a crop, they must be killed as they enter a crop, and this is now possible with the new persistent and systemic insecticides.

It has been shown by Broadbent *et al.* (1956), so far as potato viruses are concerned, that both contact and systemic insecticides will prevent the spread of the circulative virus of leaf-roll from infected plants within the crop. In the case of the stylet-borne potato virus Y, however, insecticides can neither prevent its introduction nor its spread within the crop, although experiments suggest that the latter can be decreased. Thus, even if spraying did not prevent the degeneration of stocks when virus Y was present, it enabled them to be kept for 3 or 4 years in an area where they would normally degenerate in 2 years. Insecticides can do little to prevent the introduction of virus into a crop, and these trials showed that when infective aphids land on a sprayed crop they can infect plants before they die. Furthermore, although non-infective aphids arriving upon a sprayed potato crop would be killed before they could acquire and transmit a circulative virus like that of leaf-roll, they can often acquire and transmit a stylet-borne virus, like potato virus Y, before dying.

More recently, because of the damage to potato crops by the spraying machinery, experiments have been carried out on soil-applied granular insecticides such as dimethoate, phorate, and disulphoton, or with menazon sprayed on the tubers before planting. A single application at planting effectively kept aphids from colonizing the plants for 3 months and was an effective as DDT in limiting virus spread (Burt *et al.*, 1960; Broadbent and Burt, 1962).

Among other successful cases of control of virus vectors by insecticides, quoted by Broadbent (1964), are the use of demeton-methyl against strawberry viruses (de Fluiter, 1958) and of parathion sprays against pea enation mosaic in peas (Davis *et al.*, 1961).

The incrimination of root-feeding nematode worms as vectors of numerous plant viruses of economic importance necessitates a new approach to vector control. Murant and Taylor (1965) have experimented with chemical treatment of the soil to prevent transmission of tomato black-ring and raspberry ringspot viruses by the nematode *Longidorus elongatus* (de Man). In untreated soil, after an over-winter fallow, the nematodes lost their infectivity but regained it in the spring from germinating infected weed seeds. This, incidentally, emphasizes the essential role of weeds in the spread of nematode-transmitted viruses. In soil treated with D-D (dichloro-propane-dichloro-propene, Shell D-D), with or without a surface seal of solubilized xylenols, at 400 lb/acre, 95 per cent of the *L. elongatus* were killed. This treatment and that with 20 per cent quintozene (20 per cent pentachloro-nitrobenzene) at 1,200 lb/acre prevented transmission of virus to Talisman strawberries throughout the 4-year experiment. After the first year, both D/D and quintozene treatments led to significant increases in crop, reaching 130 per cent in the third fruiting season.

Similar experiments to prevent the spread of *Arabis* mosaic viruses by the nematode *Xiphinema diversicaudatum* (Micol.) were carried out by Harrison *et al.* (1963). They used D-D and methyl bromide; virus infection in later planted strawberry crops was reduced by up to 97 per cent depending on the number of *X. diversicaudatum* surviving.

*Breeding Resistant Varieties of Crops*

One of the promising methods of control lies in the production of virus-immune or resistant varieties of plants. This is a long-range method and for it we must look to the plant breeder. Some success has already been achieved. Several good varieties of mosaic-resistant sugar-cane have been produced, known as the POJ strains, and the substitution of these for susceptible varieties in most of the sugar-growing areas has reduced the disease to one of small importance, although at one time it threatened the very existence of the sugar-cane industry. Similarly with the sugar-beet in the U.S.A., the curly-top disease became so serious that in large areas of the Union the growing of sugar-beet had to be abandoned. However, by the combination of a number of strains selected for resistance, varieties have been produced (U.S. Nos. 1, 33, and 34) which have a fair degree of resistance to curly-top and are reasonably satisfactory as regards sugar content. With the partial solving of the curly-top sugar-beet problem, the plant breeder was then faced with the same situation in beans and some success has been achieved here, also, with the production of curly-top-resistant beans.

In England, many parts of Europe, and now in the U.S.A., virus-yellows is also a serious disease of sugar-beet. This is a very difficult problem to tackle because no factor of resistance to the virus which might be used in breeding seems to exist either in the wild beet, *Beta maritima*, or in any varieties of the sugar-beet itself. Russell (1960) found no resistance in 100,000 seedlings tested, so that attention was directed to finding seedlings which showed tolerance.

Strains of cotton of the Sakel type resistant to the leaf-curl disease have been evolved, and these seem to combine vigour and fruitfulness with a high degree of resistance.

The production of a virus-resistant variety of potato is a problem of the greatest importance, but the position is complicated by the large number of different viruses to which the potato plant is susceptible.

The choice before the breeder is to develop resistant, tolerant (carrier), or intolerant varieties. The resistance may be of two kinds, to the virus or the vector; thus some varieties of cotton are resistant to the whitefly vector of leaf-curl rather than to the virus (Tarr, 1951).

The disadvantages of the carrier or tolerant types are their liability to act as a source of infection to other susceptible varieties, the fact that a second virus infection added to the carried virus is liable to produce a more severe disease than otherwise would be the case, and the possibility of a mutation in the carried virus to a more virulent type. The aim behind the development of intolerant varieties is to make them so susceptible to the virus or viruses in question that they are killed outright. The virus is thus destroyed with its host and cannot spread farther.

In the U.S.A., a potato seedling, No. 41956, has been produced which is not only resistant but appears to be actually immune from infection with potato virus X, the most widespread of all potato viruses.

Breeding for some form of resistance to virus X and the other important potato viruses, leaf-roll, and virus Y, has been carried on in Scotland (Cockerham, 1958), in the U.S.A. (Ross, 1958), in New Zealand (Hutton, 1952), and at other centres. It was shown by Stelzner (1950) that an apparent immunity from virus X existed in the wild potato *Solanum acaule*, and breeding experiments with this and *S. demissum* have been carried out by Cockerham (1958). *S. stoloniferum* is field-immune (killed by) to potato virus Y and the genetics of this type of reaction have been studied by Ross (1958).

*Cure of Virus-infected Plants*

Two methods of eliminating the virus from infected plants are considered here, firstly inactivation of the virus by heat and secondly by chemicals.

The first experiments on heat therapy were made by Kunkel (1936), who subjected peach trees, infected with peach-yellows, little peach, red suture, and rosette, to temperatures of 35°C. The trees were kept at this temperature for a fortnight or longer, and the time necessary was longer for large trees than for small; it was easier to destroy the virus in the top of the trees than in the roots. Kunkel also used an alternative method of soaking dormant trees for 10 minutes in hot water at 50°C.

That the trees were actually cured of the disease is shown by the fact that scions from the treated trees produced no disease when grafted on to a virus-free tree. Moreover, cured trees could be re-infected with the viruses, which shows there was no question of attenuation or masking of infection. Later, Kunkel (1941) showed that the virus of aster-yellows could also be destroyed by heating the host plant, but the treatment could only be applied to certain plants such as periwinkle, *Vinca rosea*, and *Nicotiana rustica*, which could survive being grown at 40°C for 2 weeks.

Since these pioneer experiments, about thirty or more viruses have been eliminated from plants by heat therapy, but only one or two examples can be given here and the reader is referred to a review by Kassanis (1957a) for an excellent survey of the whole subject. Ratoon stunt, a serious virus disease of sugar-cane in Queensland, is now controlled on a commercial scale by exposing the setts for 2 hours in hot water at 50°C. Over 2,000 tons of cane can be given the hot-water treatment in wire baskets, holding a ton at a time, immersed in special tanks (Hughes, 1954; Greenaway, 1956). Kassanis (*loc. cit.*) has shown that the leaf-roll virus is inactivated in potato tubers after 20 days at 36°C, but when potato plants, similarly infected, are treated in the same way both they and their tubers remain infected.

Posnette and Cropley (1958) have carried out experiments on the heat-inactivation of strawberry viruses in some twenty varieties of strawberries. Treatment, up to 50 days' duration at 37°C, inactivated the mottle virus, though the time needed for permanent inactivation of the virus varied considerably. Elimination of crinkle virus, though effected in 9 days in the variety Huxley's Giant, required 30 to 50 days in other varieties. The yellow-edge virus appears more difficult to eradicate; some plants are apparently cured after 26 days but relapse more than a year later. Vein-chlorosis virus is also as hard to eliminate as that of crinkle.

Budsticks from sweet cherry (variety Lambert) infected with necrotic rusty mottle virus were treated in a hot-water bath at 50°C for 10, 13, and 15 minutes, and at 52°C for 5, 8, and 10 minutes. Virus inactivation occurred in all treatments. Seven of ten Lambert trees that received buds heated at 50°C for 15 minutes and at 52°C for 10 minutes survived for at least 2 years (Nylands, 1959).

Kassanis and Posnette (1961) consider that degradation and synthesis of virus take place continuously, and that multiplication of some viruses is completely inhibited at 36°C while inactivation still continues, so that ultimately the plant is freed of virus. They suggest that inactivation is not a direct effect of temperature on the virus, but that some system in the plant takes part in the inactivation.

At the moment there is no well-established example of the practical control of a plant virus disease by means of a chemical acting on the virus in the host. The principle underlying the application of chemical therapeutics is that multiplication of a virus can be delayed by compounds which interfere with the nucleic acid metabolism. If nucleic acids are the most important part of viruses and the bases the most important part of nucleic acids, it seems reasonable to look for virus-inhibitory agents among synthetic analogues of those natural bases. For this reason, Matthews (1954) used 8-azaguanine and found that when sprayed on to plants it had quite a marked effect on the spread of virus within the plant. It was found most effective against the viruses of lucerne and cucumber mosaics in the tobacco plant. Later, Matthews (1955) carried out experiments on the inhibition of the development of turnip yellow mosaic virus, again using 8-azaguanine. These experiments suggested that, as with tobacco mosaic virus, the incorporation of the base into the nucleic acid of the turnip yellow mosaic virus renders a proportion of the virus particles incapable of initiating infection.

Thiouracil is another substance which inhibits to a certain extent the initial multiplication of several viruses in growing plants. There is no evidence, however, that it affects the virus content of systemically infected plants. Kassanis and Tinsley (1958) carried out some experiments on the effect of this substance on potato virus Y growing in normal tobacco tissue-cultures. They succeeded in freeing the cultures of the virus by growing them for 3 weeks or more on media containing 100 mg/l of thiouracil. Progenies from these cultures were still free of detectable virus 1 year after the treatment.

Experiments with 6-azauracil suggest that the analogue does not affect the multiplication of tobacco mosaic virus but there may be impaired transport from cell to cell (Dijkstra and van Rensen, 1967).

The inhibition of plant viruses by growth regulators has been studied by Raychaudhuri *et al.* (1967). They found that *in vivo* these compounds reduce the multiplication of several viruses including potato viruses X and Y and wound-tumour and tobacco mosaic viruses.

Although the chemotherapy of plant virus diseases is only beginning, the results achieved so far are at least suggestive that some practical applications of the method will be developed in the future. For a comprehensive survey of the chemotherapy of plant virus diseases, the reader is referred to a review by Matthews and Smith (1955).

*Special Methods of Propagation*

By taking advantage of the rate, or lack, of movement of a virus in a plant, it is sometimes possible to propagate from tissues which are temporarily free of invading virus. This is a useful technique in cases of valuable plants or where it is desired to build up a virus-free clone of a particular variety.

For example, virus-free plants from dahlias infected with the virus of tomato spotted wilt may be obtained by taking cuttings from the tips of shoots as they arise from the tubers. At such a time of rapid growth, the movement of the virus fails to keep pace and there are often a few inches of tissue not yet reached by the virus (Holmes, 1948).

Since some viruses fail to invade the growing-point, the apical meristem may be cut off and grown in tissue culture (Morel and Martin, 1952, 1955). Morel (1967) states that cultivation of stem apical meristem *in vitro* requires gibberellin and high ionic concentration of potassium and ammonium. When large enough, the plantlets can be transferred to soil and a virus-free plant obtained. By this method, potato plants of the variety King Edward have been obtained free of the paracrinkle virus with which all commercial stocks of this variety are infected. This is of considerable interest since no King Edward potato plant had previously been seen without the latent paracrinkle virus. All attempts made previously to eliminate the virus, by radiation or by heat treatment, had failed. By a similar technique 'Arran Victory' potatoes have been freed of virus S (Kassanis, 1957b).

Morel (1967) gives the following information on the use of this technique.

*Potato*. Plants obtained from meristem cultures of clones infected with viruses A and Y were found to be 85 to 95 per cent virus-free, but all clones infected with viruses S or X were still contaminated (but see Kassanis (1957b) on virus S). To obtain the meristem cultures, the tubers were germinated and maintained for one month at 39°C, after which the meristem was excised and cultivated *in vitro*.

*Dahlia*. The viruses of both tomato spotted wilt and dahlia mosaic were easily eliminated by meristem culture.

*Carnation*. The technique has been most successful with this plant; all carnation viruses including those of mottle, ringspot, vein-mottle, streak, and the latent virus have been eliminated by meristem culture without previous heat treatment.

*Chrysanthemum*. Of viruses attacking this plant, virus B, vein-mottle, and green-flower viruses have been eliminated.

*Narcissus*. About 60 per cent of cultures from plants with *Arabis* mosaic virus were freed of the virus.

## References

ADANSON, M. (1757) *Histoire naturelle du Sénégal*. Paris: Coquillages Bauche.

BAWDEN, F. C. (1964) *Plant Viruses and Virus Diseases*. 4th ed. pp. 312–27. New York: Ronald Press Co.

BRANDES, J. and BERCKS, R. (1965) *Adv. Vir. Res.* 11, 1–24.

BROADBENT, L. (1964) in *Plant Virology*. pp. 330–64. Eds. M. K. Corbett and H. D. Sisler. Gainesville: Univ. of Florida Press.

BROADBENT, L. and BURT, P. E. (1962) *Proc. Brit. Insecticides and Fungicides Conf.* 1961. 1, 81.

BROADBENT, L., BURT, P. E., and HEATHCOTE, G. D. (1956) *Ann. appl. Biol.* 44, 256–73.

BROADBENT, L., HEATHCOTE, G. D., and MASON, E. C. (1958) *Plant Path.* 7, 53–5.

BROADBENT, L. and MARTINI, C. (1959) *Adv. Vir. Res.* **6**, 93.

BURT, P. E., BROADBENT, L., and HEATHCOTE, G. D. (1960) *Ann. appl. Biol.* **48**, 580.

COCKERHAM, G. (1958) *Proc. 3rd Conf. Pot. Cir. Dis.* Wageningen. (1957) pp. 199–203.

DAVIS, A. C., McEWEN, F. L., and SCHROEDER, W. T. (1961) *J. Econ. Entomol.* **54**, 161.

DE FLUITER, H. J. (1958) *Mededel: L. Landbouwhoogeschool Gent.* **23**, 745.

DIJKSTRA, J. and VAN RENSEN, J. J. S. (1967) *Internat. Sympos. Plant Pathology.* New Delhi. pp. 91–2. Indian Pathol. Soc. Publ.

GIBBS, A. J., HARRISON, B. D., WATSON, D. H., and WILDY, P. (1966) *Nature,* **209**, 450–4.

GREENAWAY, S. (1954) *Proc. Queensland Soc. Sugar-Cane Technol.* p. 201.

HARRISON, B. D., PEACHEY, J. E., and WINSLOW, R. D. (1963) *Ann. appl. Biol.* **52**, 243.

HOLMES, F. O. (1939) *Handbook of Phytopathogenic Diseases.* Minneapolis: Burgess.

HOLMES, F. O. (1948) *Phytopathology.* (Abstr.) **38**, 314.

HOLMES, F. O. (1948) in *Bergey's Manual of Determinative Bacteriology.* 6th ed. Baltimore: Williams and Wilkins Co.

HOPKINS, J. C. F. (1932) *Rhodesia Agric. J.* **29**, 680.

HUGHES, C. G. (1954) *Int. Sugar J.* **56**, 338.

HUTTON, E. M. (1952) *Austral. J. agric. Res.* **3**, 362–71.

KASSANIS, B. (1957a) *Adv. Vir. Res.* **4**, 221–41.

KASSANIS, B. (1957b) *Ann. appl. Biol.* **45**, 422–7.

KASSANIS, B. and POSNETTE, A. F. (1961) *Recent Advances in Botany,* 1961. p. 557.

KASSANIS, B. and TINSLEY, T. W. (1958) *Proc. 3rd Conf. Pot. Virus Dis.* Wageningen. (1957) pp. 153–5.

KENNEDY, J. S. (1958) *Entomologia.* **1**, 50–65.

KUNKEL, L. O. (1936) *Phytopathology.* **26**, 809–30.

KUNKEL, L. O. (1941) *Amer. J. Bot.* **28**, 761–9.

LWOFF, A., HORNE, R. W., and TOURNIER, P. (1962) *Compt. Rend.* **254**, 4225–7.

MacCLEMENT, W. D. and RICHARDS, M. G. (1956) *Can. J. Botany.* **54**, 793.

MATTHEWS, R. E. F. (1954) *J. gen. Microbiol.* **10**, 521–32.

MATTHEWS, R. E. F. (1955) *Virology.* **1**, 165–75.

MATTHEWS, R. E. F. and SMITH, J. D. (1955) *Adv. Vir. Res.* **3**, 51–148.

MAYR, E. (1953) *Ann. N.Y. Acad. Sci.* **56**, 391.

MOREL, G. (1967) *Internat. Sympos. Plant Pathol.* New Delhi. pp. 100–1. Indian Pathol. Soc. Publ.

MOREL, G. and MARTIN, C. (1952) *C. R. Acad. Sci. Paris.* **235**, 1324.

MOREL, G. and MARTIN, C. (1955) *C. R. Acad. Agric. France.* **41**, 472.

MÜLLER, H. J. (1956) *Sitzber. deut. Akad. Landwirtsch. Berlin.* **5**, 1.

MURANT, A. F. and TAYLOR, C. E. (1965) *Ann. appl. Biol.* **55**, 227–37.

NYLANDS, G. (1959) *Phytopathology,* **49**, 157–8.

PEREIRA, H. G. (1966) *Nature.* **210**, 149–50.

POSNETTE, A. F. and CROPLEY, R. (1958) *J. hort. Sci.* **33**, 282–8.

RAYCHAUDHURI, S. P., MISHRA, M. D., SUBBARAYUDU, S., and MUKHERJEE, A. K. (1967) *Internat. Sympos. Plant Pathology.* New Delhi. pp. 57–8. Indian Pathol. Soc. Publ.

RIBBANDS, C. R. (1962) *Nature.* **195**, 1230–1.

ROSS, A. F. (1958) *Proc. 3rd Conf. Pot. Vir. Dis.* Wageningen. (1957) pp. 204–11.

RUSSELL, G. E. (1960) *Brit. Sugar-Beet Rev.* **28**, 163.

SCHWARZ, R. (1959) *Phytopathol. Z.* **35**, 238.

SEVERIN, H. H. P. and FREITAG, J. H. (1938) *Hilgardia.* **11**, 495.

SIMONS, J. N. (1957) *Phytopathology.* **47**, 139.

SIMONS, J. N. (1960) *Phytopathology.* **50**, 424.

SMITH, K. M. (1937) *A Textbook of Plant Virus Diseases.* 1st ed. London: J. & A. Churchill.

SMITH, K. M. (1957) *A Textbook of Plant Virus Diseases.* 2nd ed. London: J. & A. Churchill.

STELZNER, G. (1950) *Z. Pflzücht.* **29**, 135–58.

TARR, S. A. J. (1951) *Leaf-Curl Disease of Cotton. Commonwealth Mycol. Inst.* 55 pp.

VARNEY, E. H. (1967) *Internat. Sympos. Plant Pathol.* New Delhi. pp. 32–3. Indian Phytopathol. Soc. Publ.

# Author Index

# Subject Index

163